the mothercare guide to

SLEEP

— AND —

WAKEFULNESS

Heather Welford

Conran Octopus

Project editor	Jane O'Shea
Editor	Carole McGlynn
Art editor	Peter Cross
Project assistant	Dawn Sirett
Production	Sonya Sibbons
Illustrators	Stuart Trotter
	Will Giles and Sandra Pond
Jacket photograph	Julie Fisher

**First published in 1990 by
Conran Octopus Limited
37 Shelton Street
London WC2H 9HN**

© text 1990 Conran Octopus Limited

ISBN 1 85029 261 2

Typeset by Litho Link Ltd, Powys, Wales
Printed by Eagle Colourbooks Ltd, Scotland

Contents

Introduction

Sleep problems can take many forms, and there are as many different causes as there are possible solutions. Whatever kind of sleep disturbance affects your child – a baby who still wakes and cries several times a night, a toddler who resists bedtime or wakes at the crack of dawn, an older child who has nightmares – they all take their toll on the parents. Parents of sleepless children suffer from anxiety – as well as extreme fatigue. There is nothing quite like the despair and sense of loneliness you experience when trying to comfort your child in a cold bedroom in the early hours – night after night.

Most people start parenthood unprepared for the negative side of a new baby – the broken nights and exhausting days. If these persist beyond the earliest weeks and months, new parents often blame it on themselves, and feel they must be doing something wrong. But this is not the case and there is absolutely no reason to feel any sense of guilt. Babies do not, unfortunately, come into the world with a ready-programmed body clock. If they did, this would enable them to know the difference between night and day and to sleep longer and more deeply during the hours of darkness right from the beginning. Very few babies are like this – and none are like this all the time. Even so-called 'good' babies have their off-days, when nothing keeps them happy for long, and when sleep – the one thing you long for – is the very thing the baby seems to fight.

Sleep and Wakefulness covers all forms of wakeful behaviour and sleep-related problems, and will convince you that you are not alone by any means. Even if it sometimes seems to you that every other baby you know or hear about sleeps through the night without fail, the reality is different: there are in fact many, many parents in the same desperate position as you.

This book gives positive guidelines for how to cope with wakeful nights, so there is never any need to feel that you cannot do anything about your child's sleeplessness. You don't have to go through months, or even years, of helpless despair and exhaustion. The many realistic and practical suggestions in the book will help you and your child either to solve the problem, or to cope better and more harmoniously while it lasts.

All the experiences outlined in this book happened to real people. My own three children have, over the years, given me the chance to know about wakeful nights and bedtime awkwardness at first hand. Many mothers and fathers among my friends and family have shared both their sleep-related problems and their solutions with me. And the readers of *Parents* magazine who have written to the Can We Help? column I have edited for several years, have put the subject in an even broader spectrum. They – along with the panel of experts – have helped to make this column an important source of support to many young families. I thank the publishers of *Parents* magazine for giving me permission to use edited extracts from these letters within the text of this book.

I have talked to many people whose one-time babies, toddlers and pre-school children are now somewhat older, as this gives an encouraging perspective on the whole issue of sleeplessness. Your children *will* eventuallly learn to give you the unbroken nights you long for – I hope that reading this book will hasten the day.

Sleep and Wakefulness is one of a series of Mothercare Guides that covers topics of immediate interest to parents of young children. The books are all fully illustrated and offer clear and straightforward guidance on practical aspects of everyday childcare. The other titles available in the series are listed on the back jacket of this book.

All the information in these books applies equally to male and female children and, to reflect this, the pronouns 'he' and 'she' have been used in alternate chapters. This book addresses itself to parents of both sexes too – a sleepless child is a problem that has to be shared as far as possible and a father who is up half the night is likely to feel just as concerned – and exhausted – as the child's mother. The term 'partner' has been used throughout the book in preference to the less flexible terms, husband and wife.

A new baby brings all sorts of joys as well as tribulations — and certainly changes your lives for ever.

The wakeful baby

Babies vary widely in the amount of sleep they need. After the first week, when most babies tend to sleep more than they will do ever again, a newborn baby will sleep anything from a total of eight to 18 hours out of 24. Some babies sleep for a long period each time they close their eyes; others catnap fitfully.

THE FIRST WEEK

Your baby will probably spend the first one, two or three days after the birth sleeping apparently soundly for most of the day and night. She may or may not show much interest in feeding.

By day four or five, things will be looking rather different. Your baby will be both more wakeful, and more hungry. Because nature arranges things this way, your breasts begin producing milk (previously, they have made colostrum, a rich and valuable fluid that's perfect for a baby in the first days of life). If you're bottle-feeding, you will find your baby takes more at each feed.

Around this time, you may notice your baby beginning to respond to day and night by having her longest sleep during darkness – though she certainly won't sleep through. She may feed six to ten times in 24 hours. Some babies feed more often than this, and all babies will have occasional days when they need to feed more. Breastfed babies tend to feed more frequently than bottle-fed ones, both at this stage and well beyond. This is because breast milk is digested quickly, and also because frequent feeding is needed to establish the milk supply at first. Breastfed babies may appear to want to feed more often, simply because they enjoy the sensation of sucking on the breast.

Some babies, especially those who have had a difficult or traumatic birth, may continue to be sleepy most of the time for longer than the first two or three days. Your milk will come in, but there might be little response from the baby who falls asleep after the first few token sucks. Your breasts feel hot, full, tense and generally uncomfortable as a result. Ask a midwife's advice on coping with this. She is likely to suggest that you express a little milk to make your breasts comfortable. Keep offering the breast to your baby, however, and she will soon perk up.

Small babies

Pre-term babies, babies who have a much lighter-than-average birthweight, babies who have spent some time in special care before coming home because of illness or surgery, as well as twins and triplets, sometimes stay at the newborn 'sleepy' stage for a longer time, because they are adjusting to the outside world. But they will tend to start waking up more frequently as they grow. This can be a bit of a shock for a parent who has got used to an apparently contented baby, who slept and fed and did little else, but it's actually a sign that your baby is developing well. Ask your doctor or health visitor for reassurance.

Q Can babies actually know when they're in different surroundings? My baby was very calm in hospital, but for the first couple of nights at home he seemed very unsettled and needed a lot of comforting before he finally went off to sleep.

A *Yes, this is something a lot of parents observe, though nobody can be certain exactly what babies can absorb and understand. Whether it's the different smells, sights and sounds of home, something seems to get through and cause some babies to become agitated for a day or so after leaving hospital. Most parents find the most soothing response is to offer comfort and reassurance, which will let your baby know that you are his source of security and that he can feel relaxed with you.*

Other babies are wakeful, and possibly distressed, in the first days after birth. They seem reluctant to sleep and want to feed all the time. This is nothing to worry about; offer the breast to your baby as often as is necessary to calm her. Most breastfed babies derive great comfort from simply sucking on the breast. If you're bottle-feeding your baby, you may be advised to try a dummy or else water in a bottle to keep her happy in between proper bottle-feeds.

Your baby may start waking up more frequently and hungrily *before* your milk comes in – and cry because you don't yet have the milk for her. Don't assume that you have a sleepless baby. Keep offering her the breast. Within a day or so – and usually less – her appetite and your milk supply are likely to be in step with each other.

While you try to get some household tasks done, your baby may make the most of his vantage point in a bouncing cradle.

EARLY WEEKS AND MONTHS

This is when babies begin to show differences in their sleep needs! The baby who started off placid may begin to keep you awake night after night, and drained during the day. On the other hand, the baby who screamed in hospital and only ever fell asleep as a result of exhaustion may gradually become calmer and more predictable.

In the first few weeks, babies usually sleep between feeds – but some may only snooze for a short time, and others may fall asleep while sucking and then stay asleep until their tummy wakes them up for the next session. Some breastfeeding mothers will notice there are times when it's difficult to say when one feed ends and another begins; without a long nap in between, some feeds appear to slide into each other. But during this period the baby will move towards a pattern where she spends more time awake in the daytime and more time asleep at night. By four months old, many babies are sleeping roughly twice as long at night as they do in the day.

From the age of about two to three weeks, you will notice there is a particular time of day (or night) when your baby is almost always awake. For most babies this is the evening. Some babies, however, are wakeful for most of the day, and only ever take small catnaps. You may find this especially demanding, because even a baby as young as this can make it clear she needs your company and attention. Try putting your baby down to sleep between feeds but be aware that this will not work if your baby isn't tired, is still hungry, or is simply unhappy on her own.

How your day is spent

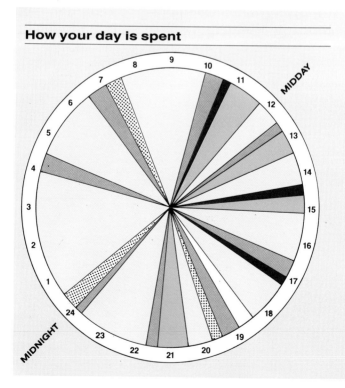

Sleep safety

▶ Always lock a rocking cradle, by means of a screw, or wedging the rockers, when you leave the baby to sleep.

▶ Never put your baby's chair on a raised surface – always have it on the ground. Even slight movements can cause a raised chair to topple over.

▶ A carrycot should be on a special stand, or on a stable surface against a wall, or on the floor. From the age of about three months, a Moses basket or carrycot should only be used on the floor.

▶ The cot should have high sides and ends to stop a baby climbing out. The spaces between cot bars should be no less than 25mm (1in) and not more than 60mm (2⅜in) to prevent the baby wriggling out or getting her head jammed.

▶ Don't let your baby become too hot at night or during her daytime sleeps. Not only will she be uncomfortable, but she may develop a heat rash. Overheating can be dangerous. Indoors she should always have her head uncovered, and only enough layers to keep her warm. Never wrap her up so snugly that she has hardly any areas of skin exposed. Feel the back of your baby's neck or her chest to check: they should feel pleasantly warm; if they feel hot or sticky, take off a layer.

▶ Check that there are no long cords or ties — on the baby's clothing, on cot bumpers or other cot furnishings, or on cot toys — that could get caught around her neck.

▶ Make sure you do not leave toys with sharp edges in the cot.

The 24-hour clock (left) is a diagrammatic representation of how much time a young baby takes up. It clearly shows how demanding of your time a baby can be, and how unrealistic it is to aim to get a hundred other tasks done during the day.

It is far better to accept that, at this early stage at least, your time is effectively the baby's, and you will be fully occupied catering for his basic needs.

This particular clock represents a day in the life of Jack, aged five weeks. Like many babies of his age, his routine is far from settled, and any period of sleep is likely to be broken by short, wakeful bouts. The longest continual period Jack spent asleep was three hours. It usually took a lot of settling to get him down to sleep, as he would cry and make little animal noises for a time when put down in his cot.

Jack cries and needs comforting frequently and, since he often possets after a feed, he also needs to be changed regularly.

A mid-afternoon walk entertained Jack for a period of time, while enabling his mother to do some shopping en route. And an early evening bath helped to tire and relax him, prior to him being put down to sleep.

Key

☐	Sleeping
☐	Feeding
☐	Playing/settling
▦	Changing/settling
■	Changing
☐	Bathing

Coping with your baby's wakefulness

For the time being, it is probably easiest for you to accept that your baby wants to be with you during her wakeful times. Trying to wipe out evening wakefulness, especially, is generally unsuccessful early on, but there are ways to help you cope with this wakeful stage.

▶ Evening wakefulness presents particular difficulties because you usually aim to get a lot done, and yet your energies are at their lowest level at this time of day. Aim at least to prepare an evening meal before your baby is likely to need attention – even if you have to eat it with her in your arms.

▶ Place your baby in a small baby chair (checking that the one you use is suitable for a young baby) while you get on with tasks around the house, so that you can talk to her, and you can see each other.

▶ Try carrying your baby in a sling: some babies like the close contact with a parent's body.

▶ Share the carrying, rocking and cuddling, when it's needed, with someone else.

▶ Don't aim to have a superbly-run, sparkling clean household. Provided the bathroom and kitchen are kept reasonably hygienic, and everyone has something to eat and cleanish clothes, that's as much as anyone can expect. Accept that babies slow everything down and don't let this worry you. A routine household task which used to be done very quickly is likely to be interrupted, at best — or else put off until days later!

▶ Consciously cut down, cut out or get help with tasks like ironing, dusting, baking, washing the windows.

▶ Remember that babies can get bored. Take your baby round the room from time to time, show her her reflection in the mirror, look out of the window with her, hold up books with bright pictures in for her to look at, sing songs and rhymes, shake a rattle, ring a little bell or a jingly toy. With luck, your baby may be more contented in between these bursts of activity.

▶ Console yourself with the fact that this stage will not last for ever, and that you can edge your baby into a better, more acceptable routine in a little while (see Towards a routine, page 16).

Many babies' most wakeful period seems to coincide with the time their parents are feeling least lively!

BROKEN NIGHTS

Night feeds are a fact of life for most young babies. Minimize their disruption, and keep them as short as possible by feeding in darkness or semi-darkness and avoiding changing your baby's nappy unless she has a sore bottom. Catch up on your own sleep by going to bed earlier in the evening, and by sleeping, or at least resting, when the baby sleeps in the day. If you have a toddler who makes this impossible, you might just be able to persuade him to lie down with you in the afternoon – it's worth a try, at least.

It's difficult to say exactly how often you can expect your baby to wake up for a feed at night. If we look at the hours between, say, 11pm and 7am – the time you're likely to be used to a period of unbroken sleep – one, two or even three feeds are normal in the early weeks. In addition, you should expect the occasional 'bad' night, when one feed seems to merge into another, without much of a rest in the middle. Night feeds are likely to become less frequent as your baby grows.

Babies who scream for a long time either in the evenings or at night should be checked by a doctor. The chances are that there is nothing seriously wrong, but it's best to make sure. Try the suggestions overleaf to help your baby calm down.

Q **My baby always seems to find it more difficult to get to sleep after a busy day. I would have thought the extra hustle and bustle would make him tired, but it only seems to upset him.**

A *This isn't uncommon. Some babies get 'wound up' when they have travelled, or when other people have held them and jiggled them about, or when there's been more noise than usual. Try for a while to keep the stimulation down to a minimum – perhaps by reducing the amount of 'passing round' when friends call, or when you are out visiting. Take your baby to a quiet, shaded or darkened room to feed him when he's jumpy. A gentle bath before bed might calm him, too.*

THE RESTLESS BABY

Sometimes, you may feel that your baby is tired, yet, because she is crying and tense, she seems unable to switch off and calm down sufficiently for sleep to take over. If this is the case with your baby, you may be able to help the process along by trying one or more of the following tips. They may help her make the transition from waking to sleep.

Calming a restless baby

▶ Allow your baby to suck for as long as she wants on the breast, or offer a dummy.

▶ Wrap your baby up in a 'parcel' with a shawl or a sheet, so that her arms are held firmly and comfortably; this is known as swaddling and gives a young baby an added sense of security.

▶ Rub your baby's back while she is lying down ready for sleep.

▶ Sing softly to her or rock her.

▶ Put her in the pram to sleep and wheel her backwards and forwards.

▶ Put on a tape, record or the radio – you can buy special 'baby soother' tapes which may work for this purpose.

▶ Massage your baby to help her relax.

▶ A bath helps some babies to unwind (other babies hate this, however, and become more and more distressed, so don't insist if this is the case).

▶ Strap your baby safely in the car – either in her car safety seat or by attaching the carrycot to the back seat using special anchorage straps – and take her for a ride. The motion and sound of the car are soothing to many babies and may even lull them off to sleep.

THE CRYING BABY

Parents often wonder just what to *do* with the baby who has been fed, changed and put down in her cot – and who sobs and screams, even after repeated attempts to soothe and pacify her. You may be at the end of your tether, longing for sleep yourself and unable to guess at what might be troubling your baby. Is it cruel to let her cry?

Babies always cry for a reason, and they cannot keep themselves awake deliberately. You may hear people say 'Oh, she's just crying to be picked up' because she stops when you cuddle her. But how else can a baby tell you when she needs your arms, your milk, the security of being close to you? You may think 'She can't still be hungry' – but how do you know for sure? In the first months, babies' appetites and growth needs vary from day to day – even hour to hour.

Once your baby gets older and more used to the world, she can gradually come to terms with the fact that other people have needs to be met, and that she won't wither away from lack

Weight gain and sleep

Babies grow at different rates, and it's quite usual that a baby's weight gain is irregular from one week or fortnight to the next. This uneven weight-gain pattern is often reflected in hunger and wakefulness – especially in breastfed babies, who can feed simply according to appetite without you knowing how much has been taken each time! When your baby has a growth spurt, she will be more hungry for a few days, and possibly a lot less sleepy too. If she's had a routine of feeding and then sleeping, that may change, and she may want to feed on and off for long periods. This is especially common around the ages of six weeks and 12 weeks. After a few days, things may change once more, and your baby will become more settled.

A baby can be *too* sleepy, however. A healthy, full-term baby who is putting on weight satisfactorily is unlikely to go more than four or five hours between feeds (except possibly at night), and most need feeding far more often than this. If your baby goes longer than this between feeds because she's sleeping, then this could be a sign of illness – she may lack the energy to wake and cry for feeds. Seek advice from your doctor, midwife or health visitor if this is happening. You may be advised to start waking your baby up to feed her, in order to maintain her food intake. If you're breastfeeding, too few feeds in the first weeks may mean your milk supply isn't getting the stimulation needed to build up a really good production line.

of love or food if she has to wait for your attention. But a very young baby can't possibly understand that: she has no real memory, no sense of time, nor the confidence to know that, because you fed her when she was hungry yesterday, and because you held her close this morning, you'll do it again this afternoon. She has to make her needs known.

Leaving a baby to cry

In general, I don't think there's any reason to expect that leaving your baby to cry will teach her anything positive. You won't spoil her by meeting her very real needs for love and security, and you need not fear that your baby can learn how to manipulate you. Older children can, and do, play games like this, but a young baby, whose needs are so basic and whose understanding is so limited, is not capable of it.

There may be times, however, when you have tried everything to comfort your baby and she continues to cry. Nothing that you do keeps her happy for longer than a few minutes at a time. Persistent crying, especially a baby who screams for a long time either in the evening or at night, needs a medical check, and you need support, too. And if you have any reason to suspect your baby may be unwell, then don't be afraid to ring your doctor for help. In the meantime, if you are feeling desperate, and unable to tolerate any more, and are too tense to give your baby any real comfort, then yes – as a short-term answer – your baby's cot is a safe, clean, warm place for her. She may fall asleep exhausted – at last.

WHERE SHOULD YOUR BABY SLEEP?

For the first few weeks your baby can sleep in a crib, a cradle, a pram, a Moses basket or a carrycot, provided these are on a stable surface such as the floor. Once she becomes too big or too wriggly, however, she should be moved into a cot.

Your baby can sleep in her own room, or in your room, whichever you prefer. She will be perfectly safe sleeping with you in your bed, as long as neither of you have been drinking or have taken sleeping tablets, which would induce you to sleep too soundly. Many parents find that some nights are inevitably shared with the baby, as a means of letting everyone get some uninterrupted sleep. This does of course mean that you will have to help your baby 'unlearn' the habit of the family bed if you start to have second thoughts about it before she does! But this may not worry you if bedsharing keeps everybody happier in the short term. You can always change the routine later. (See pages 17 and 22 on setting up new regimes at bedtime and during the night.)

Bedding

An important factor in settled sleep patterns is of course being comfortable at night, and it is worth giving careful consideration to your child's bedding. You will need at least two sets of bedding for your baby's cot, though extra bottom sheets save constant washing. It's not usual to bother using a top sheet on a cot, because you'll be washing the blankets or duvet cover quite frequently.

Fitted sheets facilitate cot-making and, because they stay in place, your baby can't ruck them up during the night by moving around. Fitted stretch terry sheets are the easiest to use, with a surface that is soft and cosy for your baby. Whether you use fitted or non-fitted sheets, make sure the fabric will withstand frequent washing. Cotton or polycotton – with the addition of nylon if the sheets are stretch – are the usual fabrics. A polycotton mixture needs less ironing than pure cotton.

In addition, you will need either a washable duvet or two blankets – the choice is yours. It's quite safe to use a duvet even with a tiny baby, and their advantage over blankets is that it is difficult for a baby to get overheated under a duvet. Because it's so lightweight, a duvet can't lie too snugly round your baby so she is able to stay cosy and warm without becoming uncomfortably hot. If you use a duvet, you will need two covers for it.

Blankets are more traditional, and preferred by many parents for a young baby. Don't choose fluffy blankets (your baby can swallow the fluff, and it may also irritate her skin), and avoid those with very lacy patterns in which she could trap her fingers. Blankets should be washable; the cellular types are quick-drying, and highly effective at keeping your baby warm.

A young baby doesn't need a pillow, and expert advice is to avoid using one until the age of 12 months at least, because of the slight risk of suffocation.

Make sure the mattress is firm and that it fits your child's cot properly (reputable makes are manufactured to a standard size which is indicated on the label). Choose a mattress with at least one waterproof side. Foam mattresses are fine, provided they are made of safe (combustion modified) foam, but they won't last as long as the interior-sprung variety. Some mattresses have a vented surface at the head end and might be worth considering, as some babies sweat quite a lot when lying on a plastic-covered mattress. When buying a cot mattress, look for British Standard BS 1877.

Practical tips

▶ A muslin square or a terry nappy placed under your baby's head will save washing a whole sheet because of a slight dribble or sickness.

▶ A plastic sheet – rubber is too heavy and difficult to wash – on top of the mattress will help with a child whose nappies leak, or who isn't yet reliably dry at night. Fitted plastic sheets stay on better than the tie-on variety, but they may be more uncomfortable to lie on.

▶ A bottom sheet, plus a duvet or two blankets, will usually be sufficient to keep your baby warm, though on colder nights you may want to add another layer. Beware of letting your baby become too hot. During the day, especially in summer, or in a house that's well-heated, a single blanket or even just a top sheet will be enough.

▶ A sleeping bag or a cosy sleepsuit is useful for a baby who tends to wriggle out of her covers.

Reassuring facts

If you're feeling uncertain and lacking in confidence because your baby doesn't seem to sleep very much, or has no sleep routine, try lowering your expectations. It will help to accept that:

▶ Babies often need time to adjust to life outside the warm, comforting womb, and some crying and wakefulness in the early days is simply a result of feeling strange and confused.

▶ Babies really are very different from one another in the amount of sleep they actually need – and most babies vary day to day, and as they grow.

▶ Young babies sometimes need help to make them relax and settle to sleep – but they can't deliberately keep themselves awake.

▶ It's both normal, and natural, for a young baby to fall asleep in your arms, while sucking on the breast or bottle, or on a dummy, and to need rocking and cuddling.

▶ You can't spoil a baby by meeting her very natural need for warmth, love, security, food and company. Her needs will change as she grows . . . and she will eventually become more predictable, though this may require help from you in establishing easier routines (see page 16).

Towards a routine

The first few weeks and months of a baby's life are naturally disorganized. Each day may be completely different from the previous one, and imposing a rigid pattern on a new baby is unlikely to work without a lot of distress and false starts. But as time goes on, and feeding is better established, you can feel more confident that you and your baby can learn to adapt to each other harmoniously.

After the first up-and-down weeks, your baby may well find a routine of his own, and all you have to do is observe it and adapt to it a little yourself. However, other babies need some help to space out feeds, and to sleep and rest when it would best suit you.

There's no right moment or age to begin this process: do what feels right for you and your family. For some babies, though, around the age of four months is a reasonable time to start — though some will already have 'settled' by then anyway, without you doing anything in particular, and for others it will be too young. You can try moving your baby towards a routine at this stage and, if it doesn't work, try again in a week or so.

You may question whether your baby actually needs a routine, where each day is more or less the same, when feeds, sleeps, baths and walks in the pram follow an unchanging order. Is it better to 'know where you are' with your baby — or can you happily carry on with each day different from the one before, letting your baby decide when he wants to feed and sleep? It must be admitted that no baby ever failed to thrive without a routine. Modern life is run by the clock because of business and household commitments — but that means nothing to a baby. But many parents *prefer* and actually need to feel more organized, so that the day follows a pattern of some sort — because you and your baby are, after all, part of modern life.

" After three children, I've come to the conclusion that as long as you don't distress a baby by making him wait for feeds, or cry with hunger and loneliness, you can't do any harm by trying to arrange his routine to fit in with yours. In the end, this seems to suit everyone best. "

ENCHANTED EVENINGS

Most parents would like their baby to sleep in the evenings. But for many young babies, it's normal and natural to be awake, at least on and off, at this time. But *you* might begin to feel it's normal and natural, after a while, to have this time for adult relaxation — time on your own, time with your partner, time to

❛❛ I can remember an evening, before we had children of our own, going to some friends' for dinner. Their little girl was about nine months old at the time, and after a breast-feed from mum, dad took her upstairs to bed. We didn't see him again for another hour and a half! He said he'd made dozens of attempts to sneak away once she had dropped off, but she'd woken up every time. ❜❜

go out occasionally without the baby. Babies become a lot less mobile as they grow, so this is another reason for nudging your son or daughter into a routine of earlier bedtimes. Popping your baby into a carrycot to take with you for an evening with friends becomes more difficult by the time he is six months old.

In attempting to put your baby to bed for the evening, you need to follow a consistent procedure for at least a fortnight, in order to give the new regime a chance to work reliably.

The bedtime routine

▶ Bath your baby at more or less the same time each evening. Allow him to play a little in the water and work off some steam! Make bathtime a sociable, loving time for both of you.

▶ Put on a fresh nappy and comfortable night clothing — not garments he's had on during the day.

▶ Give your baby a bottle- or breast-feed, and let him linger as long as he wants over the feed, but without responding too enthusiastically if he becomes playful or sociable again.

▶ Put him down in his cot or wherever he sleeps, say goodnight and leave.

The hope is that your baby will learn to accept this as the pre-bedtime routine and will expect the same every evening. The main idea is to make a real distinction between daytime and night-time. You will get this idea across more forcefully if you can put your baby down to sleep wherever you expect him to spend the rest of the night. So if you've been used to putting him in a carrycot or pram for evening catnaps, and then moving him into his cot later on, stop doing this, and put him straight into his cot instead. Once your baby is on solids (you will probably start this between four and six months) you can make tea a part of the pre-bath routine.

Don't expect this 'system' to work if your baby has had a long, late afternoon nap. You might have to keep him awake by playing with him instead of letting him snooze. If you come back from the shops at five-thirty and your baby has dropped off to sleep in the buggy or pram – wake him up!

If your baby cries after you have left the room, then go to him and try to soothe him quietly. He may need some more time on the breast, or the sucking comfort of a dummy, or just the reassurance and security of your presence. Once you've soothed him, and said goodnight again you can leave – though you may have to go back several times (see page 22 for more discussion of this bedtime routine).

Some parents are happy to stay with the baby – stroking his hand or patting his back – until he falls asleep, and then creep away. This is a lovely way to comfort your baby, and it's relaxing for you too (you may even fall asleep yourself) but it can easily lead to a situation where the baby relies on this comfort to get to sleep. If you don't mind, then this commitment is fine – after all, with some babies it only takes a few minutes to lull them to sleep, and that's it for the night. But if you spend a long time, and it starts to take over the evening, alternate the 'duty' with your partner or a regular babysitter, to prevent a situation where your baby becomes distressed if you can't be there.

Q **My baby has a nap in the late morning. He won't be put down in his cot, however, but he has to lie back in his buggy and be wheeled off to sleep up and down the hall. It takes about five minutes to get him off and then he stays asleep for about an hour. Does it matter that he's not sleeping in his cot?**

A *Not at all. From around the age of six months, lots of babies need something to ease the transition between being awake and dropping off to sleep. For some it's a dummy, for others it's a special blanket to hold, or it could be sucking their thumb or finger. For your baby, it's the soothing effect of being pushed up and down. The only risk is that one day he could wake up and try to climb out of his buggy, when you weren't able to see. To avoid this danger, try lifting him out of the buggy while he's fast asleep and popping him in his cot – at least if he wakes while he's in there, he's quite safe.*

DAYTIME NAPS
Most – not all – babies and toddlers have a sleep in the day until the age of about two, and they may have more than one nap per day for a good part of their first year. After the newborn stage, when most feeds are divided by a sleep, however short, your baby may be happiest catnapping at odd times in the day – falling asleep while out in the pram or buggy, for example. However, it will be more convenient for you to know when he's likely to have a nap. Knowing this will give you some free time, and allow you to plan for certain uninterrupted activities (a series of phone calls is easier to make without a little fist pulling at the wire, for example). And for some unsettled babies, a regular routine does help both daytime and night-time wakefulness. It's certainly worth trying.

There's no reason why you shouldn't decide on the best time for your baby's naps, to suit both of you. It would be inconvenient, for example, for your baby to sleep between two o'clock and three-thirty if you have an older child to collect from school. And a morning sleep from noon until way after lunchtime can mean a very late lunch for a baby on solids. On

Q My baby seems to have his days and nights mixed up. He's three months old and he's always slept well and for a long time during the day, while being wakeful during the night. What can I do? It's exhausting looking after him.

A *This pattern isn't altogether uncommon, but you can try and change it by deliberately turning your baby's timetable round. Wake him up during the day and feed him, every two to two and a half hours. By contrast, keep night-times quiet and low key: try the evening bathtime and feed routine suggested on page 17. If you are consistent and stick at this for several days, it should work.*

the other hand, putting your baby to bed after lunch may not work if he is a heavy sleeper and you have an afternoon toddler group you'd like to visit. It is up to you to work your baby round to fitting in with your daily commitments.

It will help to look at a concrete example. Let's say you'd like your baby to have a sleep after about twelve-thirty, but at the moment he tends to catnap whenever he has the chance – in the car, out in the pram, while actually sucking on the breast or a bottle – whereas on some days he is noticeably less sleepy than on others for no apparent reason.

Establishing regular daytime naps

▶ If your baby tends to have a longish sleep in the morning, after the first proper feed of the day (or breakfast if he's taking solids), don't let him sleep for too long. Tempting though it is to let him stay asleep as long as he wants to, it will make him too lively for a sleep later on in the day. So wake him – do this gently if he's the sort of baby who objects to waking up before he feels ready – and play with him, or take him out for a short walk.

▶ Give him a 'lunchtime feed' at around midday – even if he fed only an hour or so before. Give him his solids at about this time, too, if he has them. While you're still teaching him about nap time, keep the feed quiet and relaxed, feeding, if you can, in a peaceful setting such as an upstairs bedroom. By this age, he's unlikely to take longer than half an hour over a middle of the day milk feed.

▶ When you feel he's not hungry any more, take him off the breast or remove the bottle, wind him if you're still doing that, and put him down to sleep. He is likely to be tired provided he hasn't had a long nap before – though you may need to soothe him to sleep by stroking or rocking.

You may reluctantly need to wake your baby from a daytime nap once you are trying to nudge him into a routine.

You can adapt this form of gentle manipulation to any time of the day you choose for your baby's nap. The key is not to expect him to drop off too soon after a previous sleep. It will also help to put your baby in a sleepy frame of mind if you talk to him about sleeping, about going in his cot, and tell him what a tired baby he is. Obviously, he won't understand your every word, but you'll create the right atmosphere.

Once you have established a pattern of daytime sleeps, it's unreasonable to expect your baby to be very flexible. If he misses his nap frequently, you'll have to begin the process of teaching him all over again. And if he's often expected to have his nap at different times in the day, evening bedtime is likely to be unreliable as a result.

Q **Do you think my baby needs solids? She's only three months, and I know that's considered to be on the young side for introducing foods other than milk, but she's still waking up in the night. Her weight gain is fine and she's quite healthy.**

A *There's no evidence to show that introducing solids helps a baby sleep through the night. Three months is young for solids, as you say, and if she's basically happy and healthy on breast milk alone – as the vast majority of breastfed babies still are at this age – then there's no need to give her anything else. Wait at least another month or so. If it's any consolation, many other babies of this age are still waking in the night too.*

Of course, a more flexible approach may suit you. It may not matter one way or the other to your family whether your baby has a regular sleep time or not, and it has to be said that having to fit holiday activities round a baby's nap time can be tricky. A baby who, for one reason or another, cannot have his after-lunch sleep until half past three may get very tired and grumpy by that time, and may either become too over-wrought to sleep at all, or so exhausted he sleeps for four long hours – with a new lease of life round about his normal bedtime!

On the other hand, you will have to be flexible to a degree, and learn to respond to your baby's changing needs. A 12-month-old baby is unlikely to have quite the same sort of day as he had at six months, for example. He may sleep less, perhaps only once in the day, and his night-time pattern may be quite different. Some babies start waking up again after a long period of sleeping through, while others may sleep better at night. (See pages 22 and 32 for coping with broken nights).

Q My baby used to be very placid and was a reliable sleeper. Now, at the age of six months, everything has changed. He wakes up during the night, and he cries a lot during the day when he would otherwise have had a nap. My mother says he's teething, and he does have one or two teeth coming through. Is this the reason for his changed behaviour?

A *Not everyone accepts that teething can be painful or distressing for babies – my own feeling is that it can be, but you can never be sure that teething is the reason for a particular bout of crying or wakefulness. Babies do cry for a reason, though, and any consistent and unexplained crying needs a medical check to rule out something unseen, such as an ear infection. Ask your chemist about teething gels and other simple medication, too.*

Do whatever you can to soothe and comfort your baby at these times, and try the 'routine' suggestions outlined in this chapter. It's possible that your baby would welcome the chance to go to sleep at a special time or times each day; now he's getting older, he'll find it less easy just to drop off wherever he happens to be.

SLEEPING THROUGH THE NIGHT

Many babies still wake up during the night throughout their first year. In the first few months, of course, they wake for a feed. But by four to six months your baby should be able to last about six hours at least without feeding during the night. The reasons babies wake after this are many and various: wanting a drink, teething discomfort, getting too hot or too cold, or simply feeling a need for your reassuring presence.

The trouble is that habitual night waking takes its toll on the baby's parents and you wonder if it will ever end. Reassure yourself that the longed-for ability to sleep through does come in time, and, in many cases, without you doing much about it. However, there are ways in which you can encourage your baby to stay asleep, or – more accurately – to settle himself straight back to sleep, once he has woken, without needing your help to do so.

Helping him sleep through

▶ Keep night feeds peaceful and short. Don't switch on a bright light, only change your baby's nappy if it's really necessary, and don't start any rough and tumble or boisterous playtime.

▶ Don't bring your baby downstairs or into the room where the rest of the family is once you've put him to bed.

▶ Keep a low night light on in your baby's room, and leave the door of his room open at least a little, so that he can make out familiar surroundings if he wakes.

▶ Keep one or two familiar, safe and soft toys in your baby's cot.

▶ The familiar lullaby played by a musical cot mobile may be enough to send your baby back to sleep after a brief awakening. You will need to go into his room swiftly in order to turn it on.

▶ Make sure your baby doesn't get too hot or too cold at night – if he wakes and is uncomfortable he'll find it difficult to get back to sleep easily.

▶ If your baby uses a dummy, try to take it out of his mouth as soon as he's on his way to sleep. Provided he doesn't actually fall asleep with the dummy in his mouth, you should avoid the situation where the baby falls asleep, loses the dummy, wakes and cries because it has fallen out . . . needing you to stagger out of bed, find it and pop it in again.

▶ Don't be afraid to wake your baby up in the late evening to feed him if this will help him stay asleep through the night. If he regularly wakes to feed between midnight and one o'clock, for example, see if waking him before you go to bed will fill him up sufficiently to prevent him waking you shortly after. As he grows, you can gradually shorten this late night feed, until it's hardly worth having.

Bedtime blues

Bedtime difficulties can take many forms, but they all take their toll on the parents. Whether your child objects to going to bed in the first place, or, once there, cries until you pick her up and take her out (if she's in a cot), or else repeatedly gets out of bed herself, you may feel at a loss as to how to cope. For some unlucky families, all three areas – getting to bed, settling down, and staying there – are fraught with problems.

Bedtime for your child should be a happy, cosy, friendly time, finished off with a quick tucking in of the bedclothes, a warm kiss and cuddle, and a wave at the bedroom door. Shouldn't it? All too often, the reality is somewhat different. You may be up and down the stairs, sometimes with your baby in your arms, constantly giving reassurance. Or else your child protests forcefully at the very idea of being put to bed, and her real bedtime seems to get later and later, until the only thing that finally makes her go to sleep is total exhaustion.

❝ My 14-month-old son still likes a breastfeed to settle him down to sleep at night. Occasionally, he wakes up through the night and a quick breastfeed is all he needs to get off to sleep again. It's a situation that suits us both. He doesn't sleep during the day, so by the time his bedtime comes I'm ready for a rest and breastfeeding guarantees an evening's peace. The only thing is, I feel a bit daft when I tell other mothers I'm still feeding. ❞

Many babies develop rituals associated with bedtime. These are fine in themselves – but they can develop a momentum of their own almost without you realizing it, and become more and more complicated as the weeks go by. What starts as a reasonable request to give teddy a kiss goodnight can gradually extend to demands for you to kiss every single soft toy on the shelves – even in the cupboards. And 'Just one more story' is another familiar variation on the same theme. All these rituals serve the purpose of delaying your departure.

Even if your baby started off with a period of happy and peaceful bedtimes, there's no certainty that she won't start showing this sort of behaviour at some stage in infancy or childhood. The principle behind making a fuss at bedtime is simple – it delays the moment of truth, the moment of separation, the moment of being alone for the night. To describe this as 'naughtiness' pure and simple is to ignore the fact that making a break from you can be difficult for a child; night-time, alone in her bedroom, can be hard to bear, even if her nearest and dearest are only a few feet away in another room.

The slightest creak of a floorboard could disturb your baby's hard-won sleep, so make your exit as discreet as possible.

ESTABLISHING HAPPY BEDTIMES

From a very early stage, it will help your child to settle for the night if you keep up a gentle, more or less unvaried routine each evening (see page 17). As your baby gets older she may drop the evening breast- or bottle-feed; or even if she continues with it, this may not mark the final point before sleep. But if your baby still needs a bottle or the breast to soothe her to sleep, then carry on, unless she seems to be increasing her sucking time beyond what you feel happy to tolerate. If you're still breastfeeding, don't let other people put you off if you're quite happy to continue; plenty of mothers and children carry on because they both find it pleasurable and convenient.

If your child *has* stopped sucking in the evenings, or if the evening feed is no longer the precursor of sleep, you can have a cosy time together looking at books or just talking, either in an armchair or on the sofa, or once she is in her cot or tucked up in bed. The main object is to have a peaceful, intimate and reassuring interlude just prior to the time for sleep.

What is so upsetting to parents about 'bad bedtimes' is that the situation can easily escalate until you end up resenting your child – and feeling guilty about it. You sense that no one's needs are being met: at worst, your child spends a part of every evening cross and upset because she wants more of your time and attention than you feel ready to give. And while you want to think of yourself as a kind and understanding parent, able to adapt to your child's needs and remain in control, all too often you feel you have lost both your sympathy and your control.

Q At what age can a child manage to sleep in a bed instead of a cot? Is making the change more likely to lead to disturbed nights?

A *Most toddlers seem to make the cot-to-bed transition at some time between the ages of two and three. The change may be hastened because parents need the cot for the next baby, but bear in mind that it would be wise to leave a gap between taking your toddler out of her cot and putting the new baby in it. Some babies learn how to scramble out of their cots, and in this case a bed is better for safety's sake. You can buy a bed guard that fixes on to the side of the bed, which would stop your child rolling out of bed in the first few weeks.*

But if your baby's happy enough in her cot, and hasn't yet learned to climb out, then keep her in as long as you want – or until she is too big for it. Moving a young child to a bed does sometimes lead to night (and early morning) wandering, once she discovers she can get out so easily, but usually this is short-lived. If your child starts to habitually get out of bed, follow the suggestions on page 33 for dealing with this.

On the whole, the move from a cot to a bed usually makes little difference to the sleeping and waking habits of most babies and toddlers. Sleeping in a bed may even induce better sleep, as it is more comfortable for your child, giving her extra room to move around without banging against wooden bars or ends.

Fitting in with your baby

Of course, not everybody feels that baby-led bedtimes are a bad thing. Some families simply accept the situation, at least throughout babyhood. It can suit you and your baby to allow her to remain up until she falls asleep by herself, or while sucking on the breast or the bottle. This can work perfectly well, provided your baby is bathed and changed, ready for bed, and the likely moment for her to fall asleep is not too late to fit in with your plans for the evening.

Taking this approach with a toddler or an older child, the scenario is likely to involve playing or watching television until much later, when exhaustion takes over, and she flops on the floor or in a chair. The disadvantage here is that your child may become cross and unsettled because she's tired and can't yet wind down for sleep, and you also have very little time when you're not actively looking after her. In addition, babysitters who bring their knitting in expectation of a quiet night may baulk at playing with the sticklebricks for a couple of hours or more!

BRINGING BEDTIME FORWARD

There is nothing intrinsically 'wrong' about your child going to bed late. Don't forget that in other countries, late bedtimes are quite the norm. You will have noticed if you've been abroad on holiday, how even quite young children in France, Spain and Italy, for example, stay up to share the family evening meal, and go to bed extremely late by most British parents' standards. (They may well have had a siesta earlier on in the day, of course.) This points to the fact that at least some of our childcare practices are rooted in our expectations, rather than in children's real needs. If you want to be Continental and it suits you and your child, then go ahead.

Comforters

Many children have a special comforter to help them get off to sleep – and this may continue well beyond the baby stage. Dummies are tolerated by many parents until their child is five or older – though they are then usually kept for bedtime use only. Thumb- or finger-sucking is also common from as early an age as a baby can find her thumb — and is of course perfectly normal. Lots of children have a favourite toy, blanket or piece of cloth that helps them make this transition.

On the other hand, you may well prefer to have your evenings clear of children, and to make sure that your child – once she no longer has a daytime nap – gets enough sleep at night to be alert and cheerful during the following day. You first have to decide on a suitable bedtime for your child: ask around other parents, and think about what is likely to be acceptable to your child in terms of the family routine at the end of the day. As an example, a child aged between one and three might reasonably be expected to be in bed and settled some time between six-thirty and eight o'clock. Then work towards this, following the suggestions on the opposite page. You will no

Your child's interpretation of the bedtime story may be rather different from yours.

doubt have to modify some of these, according to the age of your child and her current habits. If she's used to falling asleep at nine-thirty, you can't expect her to feel anything but outrage and surprise if you suddenly demand a bedtime three hours earlier. It would be helpful to work out a programme in advance – with your partner – so that you gradually reach the ideal bedtime, in 15- or 20-minute stages.

A firm hand at bedtime

▶ Only accept a limited number of bedtime rituals. Be faithful to these and refuse to do more. Don't be afraid to say 'no' to your child, and mean it.

▶ Put your child down in her cot or bed, and make it quite clear, by being kind but firm, that she is expected to stay there for the night. Say goodnight and leave the room.

▶ If she cries, leave her for a couple of minutes, and then return. Repeat the kind but firm goodnight and do no more than soothe her with a backrub or a quick cuddle, and a few words of reassurance – and then swiftly leave the room again.

▶ Repeat the process for as long as it takes for your child to realize that she has nothing to gain by crying. Remain firm, try not to show any irritation you may be starting to feel, and, above all, do not weaken and allow your child to get out of bed, if she is in one, or pick her up from her cot.

The great advantage of this consistent approach is that is almost always works eventually. The child knows she hasn't been abandoned, and you are not forced to hear her cry for ages. Everyone knows where they stand. The only difficulty is that it relies on you, the parents, to be firm and consistent, and to be patient enough to keep up the programme for as long as it takes. This should not be more than a fortnight or so – and it may take a lot less. Both parents must agree not to undermine the plan in any way, so it is important that you and your partner are in agreement about it in the first place. Bear in mind that you should not expect the routine to work in strange or new surroundings; this would be unfair to your child.

Less of the same

If you don't feel up to imposing a routine on your child, then you don't have to do it straight away. You may decide in the short term to put up with erratic bedtimes, with frequent running up and downstairs, with endless 'just one more' stories. One solution, if you feel you can't leave your baby or child to cry, but you don't want to spend most of every evening lying down next to a sleepy child, is to start to cut down your involvement very gradually. This may take some time, but will effectively reduce your child's dependence on you at night-time.

Night-time fears

Awkward behaviour at bedtime may have its basis in genuine fears, so don't rule out this possibility, especially if the behaviour starts suddenly. A bad dream, or some unhappy night-time experience, can make a child associate going to bed with an unpleasant event. Young toddlers can't express just why they're anxious, either.

When my youngest child was aged three, for instance, she became very nervous about going upstairs to bed in the evening. Her bedtime reluctance started a week or so after a burglary that happened during the night, when everyone was asleep. I think she was actually frightened to express her fears about the burglar – just in case we couldn't actually offer her full, cast-iron reassurance. While she was able to understand that the locks we had put on her windows offered protection, she was still worried that a burglar could get in another way.

There will also be times when you just *know* that your child is in need of a close, comforting cuddle, despite the usual 'love her and leave her' bedtime routine. It is important therefore not to be too hard and fast about your regime, but to remain open-minded and sensitive to your child's needs. Older children may sometimes need the peaceful quiet of the evening to talk to you about a special worry. See page 51 for a detailed discussion of sleep disturbances, and on how you can help your child come through them.

In stages, go from kneeling by the cot, or lying next to your child on her bed, to sitting on the floor or bed. Then start sitting on a chair beside the cot or bed and gradually move the chair nearer the door. Don't talk to her or become involved in any way, or your strategy will have the wrong effect, by making your child feel more wakeful. At first, you will still have to wait until your child is properly asleep before you leave each time. It won't work if she sees through your plan, and tries to keep herself awake in order to catch you creeping out. But eventually your child will become less dependent on your presence, almost without realizing what has happened.

Safety first

► Never let your baby go to bed with a bottle of milk or juice. There's a slight risk of choking if she should fall asleep with a mouthful of fluid. There are also harmful effects from bathing the teeth for hours on end in sweet liquid, however dilute – this can cause decay even in teeth which are not yet through the gums.

► Choose a firm mattress with holes or vents in it to enable air to circulate, so that it is impossible for the baby to suffocate (look for British Standard no. 1877).

► Never use a pillow for a baby under a year, because of the danger of suffocation.

► Use a bed guard, at least as a temporary measure, when your child first moves from a cot into a bed.

The night owl

Getting your child to go to bed happily and to stay there is one issue. But habitual waking up, and the broken nights that affect your sleep are often even more disturbing and most parents are anxious that this doesn't continue longer than necessary. All children, and all adults, wake up several times throughout the night. There are differing levels of sleep, and it's normal to wake momentarily after a period of light sleeping. Most of us are able to get back to sleep again fairly easily. Helping your child to 'sleep through' is mostly a question of teaching him that he can get back to sleep just as easily, without needing to disturb you in the process.

Never believe anyone who tells you there's a certain moment, or a special age, when a child should be sleeping through . . . and if you miss it, you've got broken nights to look forward to for the next several years. There is no such magical timing. Babies begin life *needing* to wake in the night because of hunger; they wake up because their empty tummy tells them they need to be fed. A very few babies sleep through the night — that is, they last for eight hours without needing a feed – from a few weeks old. This is unusual, and if your six-week-old baby gives you an unbroken night, enjoy it while it lasts – it may not! Sleep patterns change throughout babyhood and childhood.

Night feeds

By the age of six months, you can be reasonably sure that a healthy baby who has a good appetite during the day, whether

If you are having to take drastic steps in order to get a wakeful child back to sleep at night, it may be time to break the habit!

or not he's taking a large amount of solids, no longer needs night feeds in order to grow satisfactorily. Waking is usually associated with hunger in a young baby. However, there are babies of over six months who really wolf down a bottle at night, and those who seem to feed from the breast very hungrily at night, whose parents are certain that it's hunger that wakes them and only a full tummy that gets them to sleep again.

Lots of babies continue the habit of waking up through the night well after the stage when they're likely to be hungry, because of the comfort the night-time contact brings. It's a very common happening. About half of all one-year-olds in fact wake up and disturb their parents in the night. Many babies grow out of the tendency soon enough, without any help from you, so you may not feel that it's worth working out a strategy to combat it. But as a start, you could try the suggestions below for making night-times as calm as possible.

Q **My son's two, and he's still virtually breastfed on demand through the night. I'm quite certain his sleeping – and mine! – would improve if I could end the breastfeeding. I really would like to stop now, anyway.**

A *Yes, your toddler* is *likely to sleep better once he stops expecting to have a feed whenever he wakes up. You could simply explain to your child that breast milk is for babies and that although cuddles are 'allowed' at night, breastfeeding isn't. You will have to be firm and consistent about this, going in when he cries but refusing to use breastfeeding as a comfort. Remember that at night your resistance is often low! Hopefully he will soon stop waking up so often.*

In the end, you have to decide whether you are really committed to stopping the breastfeeding, regardless of your child's sleep pattern. If you are, it's worth running the risk that it may not make a great deal of difference to your toddler's waking. If not, you may prefer to leave it a while, in the hope that he'll soon stop by himself.

If you're breastfeeding, a comfort feed (which is all it's likely to be towards the end of the first year) is a typical and effective way of settling an older baby. Think about changing the habit, however, if your baby starts to wake up more frequently or if the comfort feeding is taking longer each time.

The situation is slightly different for a bottle-fed baby. A baby of six months or more can drink a bottle of milk very quickly and efficiently, and may only satisfy his comfort sucking needs with a much larger amount of milk. If a bottle is the one thing that gets your baby back to sleep, then it may be that he is one of the hungry babies discussed above. But if he shows no sign of giving up the night bottles, consider introducing a dummy, and gradually diluting the milk so he is taking no more than a few ounces each night. Otherwise, your baby's milk intake will be too high, and could either prevent him from eating a wide range of solid foods, or give him unnecessary calories that may cause him to put on too much weight. As with a breastfed baby, you should think seriously about changing your baby's habits if he starts to need more milk in the night, or to wake up more often than before.

Night-time comfort

It is worth checking on the following points, to ensure that your baby is comfortable at night. If he wakes up, he is then less likely to need your help in getting back to sleep again.

▶ Is your baby warm enough in his room at night? If he's a restless sleeper he may wriggle out of his bedding and end up getting chilled. A cardigan on top of his night clothes will help him to stay warmer. Creep in just before you go to bed and replace the bedding if it's come adrift or been kicked off.

▶ Does he get too hot at night? Too much bedding can make a child uncomfortably sweaty. If you are using blankets, try and change to a duvet which will help him to maintain a comfortable body temperature without cocooning him in heat.

▶ Is there a street light or a light on the landing shining into his face? Try changing the position of the cot, or making thicker curtains, if this is the case. You can buy 'blackout' lining which will keep out light on summer evenings or early mornings.

▶ Is it too dark and grim in the room when he wakes up? Use a low-wattage night light in his bedroom, or try leaving the landing light on and the door open a crack, to give him extra reassurance.

▶ Could shadows on the wall make him frightened? A child too young to talk would be unable to express a fear connected with this. Change the layout of the room, and take down anything hanging on pegs on doors to see if this makes any difference.

▶ Could your child be one of the rare children who find being in a very wet nappy uncomfortable? Rather than get into the habit of changing him at night, switch to a more absorbent type of disposable, or if you use terries put two on at night.

If you run through all these simple causes of wakefulness without it making any difference to your child's night waking, you may have to accept that, for the moment, your child is in the habit of needing night comfort from you. Equally, if you don't see the night waking as a problem, don't force yourself to think of it as one. You might be happy to offer your child the company and contact he asks for through the night, and to accept that this is the way things are at present. They may well get better of their own accord when your child feels ready. But, for some children, the 'cure' will call for more effort on your part than simply putting up with the broken nights. You will have to really work at changing the pattern.

Types of night light

Keep a low-wattage light on in your child's room all night to give him reassurance when he wakes

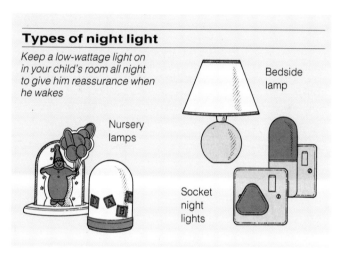

Bedside lamp

Nursery lamps

Socket night lights

BREAKING THE NIGHT-WAKING HABIT

Provided you want to, it is usually possible to persuade a baby over about nine months to a year to sleep more reliably through the night. You need to help him break old habits and start new, more acceptable ones. The older your toddler or child, the greater his determination to stick to his night-comfort habits, whatever form they take – whether it's breast, bottle, dummy or sharing your bed. You may need to adopt different tactics, but that doesn't mean it can't be done. You also have to be prepared to be very firm and consistent in your approach, and determined to stick to your guns, whatever happens. Bear in mind that your resolve is bound to be weaker in the middle of the night.

Assuming that you do want to have peaceful nights from the time you go to bed until a reasonable hour the next morning, and that you have made sure your child's bedroom is comfortable, and ruled out all the possible hitches outlined above, the first and most important thing is to stop, or modify, doing whatever you currently do when your child wakes up. The principle behind this is to stop making it worth your child's while to disturb you, without allowing him to feel he's been let down or ignored. In a sense, anything nice that happens on waking is likely to reinforce the habit of waking. So remove the reward, or reduce its power.

Cutting down

▶ If you take your baby a drink, make it a small one. If he drinks juice, or milk, at night, gradually water it down. If you breastfeed your baby, make the feed as short as possible – just give one side, for example, and stop as soon as you see his eyelids flicker asleep.

▶ If you sing a string of nursery rhymes, just sing one or two and then stop.

▶ If you take your baby out of his bedroom, then stop doing this. Pick him up if you have to but stay in the room with him.

▶ If you lie down with him on his bed or elsewhere, then just sit.

▶ If you take him into your bed, stop doing it; if you let him just climb in, take him straight back.

▶ If you play games or read stories, reduce your contact to a short, quiet chat.

▶ If you take him out for a ride in the car, stop doing it, and rock him in your arms instead (if he's already too heavy for this, sit in a chair and rock backwards and forwards – a rocking chair obviously makes this easier).

In the end, with many children, reducing the 'reward' simply isn't enough. You have to dilute it, as it were, so much that it's hardly recognizable. The quiet chat instead of the games and stories may have to become no more than a quiet 'Go to sleep'. The picking up and cuddling may have to be reduced to a few pats on the back. The short breastfeed may have to go entirely before the child learns that he doesn't have to suck in order to get back to sleep.

With a child over about 18 months, you can begin some sort of explanation for your new regime. During the day, when you're in a sympathetic mood, tell your child how mummy and daddy need to stay asleep in the night or else they get cross and tired the next day – and explain to him that you're going to help him stay asleep as well. The younger the child, the more simple the explanation needs to be, and the more often you will have to repeat it. It's unreasonable to expect your child to make up his mind, unselfishly, to help you out in this. But giving a rationale for your actions will make them less arbitrary and slightly more understandable. With an older child, you can adopt a somewhat different approach (see pages 44-46), by reasoning with them or offering incentives if they sleep through.

Provided you're consistent about keeping night-time contact to an absolute minimum, this process is likely to be successful after a few nights, for some children, and a few weeks, for others. It is a good idea to keep a sleep diary before and after you start your new regime, to detect how much effect – on the number of wakings, length of time spent awake – your measures are having. An example of a sleep diary is shown on the following pages.

Use these pages to draw up a two-week sleep diary for your wakeful child, basing it on the one illustrated below.

Since it is not easy to think things through clearly in the middle of the night, keeping such a diary will enable you to detect whether there is any pattern to your child's waking. It will also let you see if your measures are having any effect, and – if they are – what kinds of improvements there have been.

Day	Woke	Settled
	11.15pm	11.30 pm Drink of juice
	3 am	3.30 am Cuddle and rocking
	6.30 am	Morning begins
MON		
TUES		
WED		
THURS		
FRI		
SAT		
SUN		
MON		
TUES		

Day	Woke	Settled
WED		
THURS		
FRI		
SAT		
SUN		
MON		
TUES		
WED		
THURS		
FRI		
SAT		
SUN		

Swapping beds may gain you some peace, if not the comfort to enjoy it!

Q Does diet have an effect on waking? My 15-month-old son wakes up and cries for me at least three times some nights. Nothing I've tried makes any difference and he shows no sign of outgrowing this. I'm beginning to wonder if it's something to do with what he eats – or whether he's just hyperactive.

A *If your child wakes up regularly, then you could make a note of what he's had to eat and drink the day before and see if there's a pattern at all. You might spot some connection. Try leaving out the suspect food or additive for a week and note whether it makes a difference. It's an unlikely possibility, though, in most experts' opinion. Truly hyperactive children (see page 53) are a different kettle of fish and they exhibit other symptoms than simply waking in the night.*

THE 'FAMILY BED'

There can be few parents who have never let their child share their bed. We know it can calm and comfort a child to snuggle up to mum or dad, especially after a bad dream, or when he feels unwell – and it does ensure some sleep at least. With a younger baby who cries at night, bringing him into the parents' bed may be the quickest and easiest way of settling him back again.

Whether, in principle, you let your child come into your bed whenever he wants is really up to you. Some parents are very keen on the idea of the family bed, feeling that sleeping together makes families closer and more responsive to each other's needs. Other families start off the night with the child in his own bed, and the parents in theirs, and just accept that by morning everyone will be in together. There are other variations

United front

As with any new routine, especially one you hope will change your child's habits, both parents need to be in complete agreement. If one of you is content to have the child in bed with you nightly and one of you is not, your child will feel he can exploit the differences between you. Establishing a new routine is far less likely to be successful as a result.

on these themes – the child comes into the parents' bed, and wriggles and writhes so much that one parent ends up going grumpily into the child's bed, simply to get some peace. Or the child is allowed ten minutes in the parents' bed, and – unless everyone's fallen asleep by then – is carried back to his own bed afterwards.

If you do share a bed, then be clear about the implications: your child will enjoy it and will want to repeat the experience. But, on the other hand, this isn't a habit you won't be able to break when the time's right, so it's not worth rigidly making up your mind never to share a bed in case you start something you can't stop. Bear in mind that this may take some time however: the longer you share your bed, the longer you'll have to spend insisting on un-sharing it. If you think that bedsharing is somehow connected with ill-discipline or spoiling, then you should think twice before allowing it the odd time. But in the short term there is no doubt that bringing a child into your bed will soothe him and give you a fairly uninterrupted night. Either way, you won't harm your child.

An end to bedsharing

There are practical factors that may encourage you to stop the habit of bedsharing. The still-to-be weaned breastfed toddler may increase his feeding demands by sucking on and off all night once he is in bed with you, which will prevent you sleeping fully and deeply. Very athletic toddlers who end up sleeping diagonally across the bed are not ideal sleeping companions. And once you have more than one child, the whole idea may become impractical: when you find yourself trying, unsuccessfully, to feed a new baby, soothe a fractious toddler and calm a five-year-old who has had a nightmare – all in the same bed – you may well decide that the time has come to end the family bed-share.

For whatever reason you want to stop bedsharing, you *can* do it. For several nights you may have to take your child back to his cot or bed as soon as he creeps in beside you – and if you are still taking him out of his cot to bring him in with you, simply stop doing it. It may take a while for your child to get the message, so if you know you haven't the strength to repeatedly insist, at this time, leave it for a while, and try again when you're feeling more resolute. It won't work if you are inconsistent, and insist on some occasions and not on others. But if the idea of returning to his own room is presented to him in the right way – as a stage in growing up – your child may be happy to accept it. Make sure, too, that his room is a pleasant, inviting place to go to, after the comfort and warmth of the parental bed.

SLEEP AND MEDICATION

Very mixed feelings exist amongst parents and doctors about giving drugs to help induce children to sleep. However, the fact is that lots of parents *do* obtain sleeping drugs for their children at some point – one study showed that about a quarter of toddlers have been given some medication in order to make their nights more settled.

The issue of sleeping drugs is really a matter for you to discuss with your doctor, in the context of your own child's difficulties. In the view of one leading paediatrician, prescribing sleeping medication can be seen as a sign of failure on the part of a doctor, who should instead be helping and supporting the parents through the problem, with practical advice and sympathy. Don't ever make the mistake of thinking that a drug will necessarily provide a magic solution. There are many different formulations, and different strengths, and what works with one child may not work with yours – and it may be a matter of trial and error to get the 'right' dosage and brand. Sometimes, a sleeping drug can make your child overtired and grumpy the following day.

" My doctor gave me enough of a sleeping drug for Andrew to have a dose for five nights. Things had become really bad, and I couldn't cope in the day with him. That seemed to give him the opportunity to find a new sleeping pattern, and since then he wakes only once or twice in the night. I would use it again if I had to. "

The other important thing to remember is that drugs should never be seen as a long-term answer to your child's sleep problem. The longer they are used, the less effective they become, and the dose would need to be continually increased to make them work at all – which is of course a very undesirable state of affairs. Never give your child sleeping medicine for longer than a week at a time, and then only on prescription from your doctor.

In some cases the main reason to use drugs is to guarantee a fatigued parent a whole night's sleep. Constant exhaustion can cause untold misery and stress within families. Using medication can give everyone a chance to catch up on lost sleep and, with luck, may break a vicious circle of tiredness, irritability and anxiety. Used in moderation, and only after consultation with a doctor, drugs can be an effective last resort – valuable in giving the parents a break, and some breathing space. With luck, they may also break the child's cycle of habitual waking and start off better sleeping habits. Even if they don't, and your child starts waking again once you stop the medication, refuelling your own batteries will have helped you gain the confidence and the energy to be consistent in your reactions to night-time waking, so that you encourage undisturbed nights in your child. This is really the only long-term prospect of change.

The lark

For many babies and young children, 'morning' begins at six o'clock or five-thirty, or even earlier. If you normally get up very early in the morning yourselves, your baby will simply fit in with the rest of the family. Early waking should only present a problem if your baby demands action more than, say, half an hour before you would otherwise get up.

Very young babies often wake early in the morning, but they are usually happy to have a breast- or bottle-feed and then go back to sleep again without any problem. With an older baby or toddler things are quite different – she may have the early-morning feed or drink, or you may try your usual methods of settling her, as you would if she woke during the night, but these will not lull her off to sleep. Instead, she's as bright as a button, full of beans, and quite ready to start the day. Understandably, she soon gets bored, lonely and cross if there's no one else around to share her company at this hour, and will soon cry or shout for attention.

If your child's early-morning waking is part of a general pattern of unsettled sleep, then you will have to try the various suggestions given for establishing a routine to help your child sleep through the night (see page 22). But if her early rising is an isolated problem, then there are several steps you might take to eliminate possible causes. If none of these makes any difference, console yourself that this phase should not last long.

There are several ways to lengthen the interval between your child's early rising and the time she decides she wants company!

Encouraging her to sleep later

▶ Check to see whether a regular early-morning noise could be waking your child up, such as a train passing, the build-up of traffic if you live near a busy road, or simply the dawn chorus of birds. Try moving your child's cot or bed away from the window, out of earshot. You might even consider moving her to a different room in the house if this would be quieter.

▶ If the curtains are quite thin, and light is getting through at sunrise, consider putting up thicker curtains, or lining them with a 'blackout' lining (which is actually white but lets no light through). Alternatively, use a heavy-duty blind at the window of her room.

▶ Dress your child in a sleepingbag suit at night if she tends to wriggle out of her bedclothes. She might be waking up with the early-morning cold, especially in the winter months.

▶ Try to delay her evening bedtime by an hour, in gradual stages, to see if this makes any difference to the time she wakes. This is unlikely to work in a child who is generally a poor sleeper, but is worth a try if your child simply wakes too early for comfort.

Many young children are at their liveliest and best first thing in the morning, however early they wake up.

Sometimes, toddlers get into the routine of moving their bowels on waking very early. If they have reached the stage where they find a dirty nappy is uncomfortable, or if you have encouraged them to let you know when it happens, they will then shout or cry for you to change them. This can apply to a toilet-trained child who is still in nappies at night, as well as to a toddler who is not yet trained.

There is no easy answer to this, as you'd be mistaken to try and control the time your baby passes a motion, and getting cross with your child will certainly not help the situation. You can put on a clean nappy (or pants on an otherwise trained child) and then go back to bed, hoping your child does the same, or else plays quietly in her room. This phase is unlikely to last more than a few months, and though it's a nuisance, it's no more than that.

Soaking wet nappies that leak through to the sheets can act as a stimulus to waking early. This can be countered by putting on double terries at night or by buying the most absorbent disposable you can to keep your child as leakproof as possible. Make sure you have a plastic undersheet, to prevent the mattress getting soaked. There's little else you can do to overcome this problem. Don't start limiting drinks at bedtime – your child could then wake up with a genuine thirst.

GAINING TIME IN THE MORNINGS

Very early waking – the pre-six o'clock syndrome – is usually short-lived, fortunately. Though most parents go through it at some stage, it is a habit that generally ends as the child grows more settled in her day generally. You can optimistically expect it to last only a couple of months and, while it does, you may just have to accept it and adjust your lifestyle accordingly. If your child goes through this stage during the summer months, you will probably find it easier to cope with early rising than in the dark mornings of winter.

The simplest answer to a child's early waking is of course to adjust your own timetable to fit in with your child's time clock, and to go to bed earlier in the evenings to compensate for early mornings. Many young children are at their best and their most appealing first thing, so getting up at the crack of dawn with your child does have its rewards! However, you may simply find the time your child wakes just too early for comfort.

Some parents find themselves at a loss as to how to make use of the extra time in the morning with an early-waking baby. Apart from having a leisurely breakfast together, and using the time to look quietly at books, you could even get on with housework and other tasks while the baby plays or has her breakfast. The early hours of morning, before the rest of the household is up, can seem calm and peaceful. After breakfast could be a good time to give your baby a relaxing bath – this might even induce her to go back to bed soon afterwards, refreshed and clean, for an early mid-morning sleep.

If you find it difficult to get up early in the mornings – and for many parents, the evenings are simply too precious to cut short – your aim should be to lengthen the interval between your child's own time of waking and the moment when she wakes you up by crying for you, or by coming into your room if she is already in a bed.

Occupying an early-waking baby or toddler

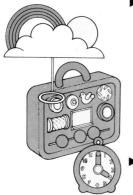

▶ Leave a drink in a bottle or a spillproof beaker by your child's cot or bed; it may be genuine thirst that wakes her, and after a drink she may be happy to stay quietly in her cot or bed for a time.

▶ Leave some books and a couple of interesting but safe toys by the cot or bed for her to reach. Vary these every few days before the novelty wears off.

▶ Make sure any toys you leave in a baby's cot are safe, with no small parts she could break off, and no strings or looped ribbons to wrap round and trap her fingers. Select toys that conform to British Standard 5665 or 3443 or which carry the Lion Mark. For a baby, choose soft toys, chunky bricks and rattles, or put an activity centre on the cot bars. Toddlers enjoy toys that are a little more challenging, though most of them like the familiarity of a favourite soft toy too.

▶ Take it in turn with your partner to go in when your child calls or cries for you, so that one of you gets a longer sleep.

Toddlers may wake up very early because they really don't *need* to sleep any more. Try limiting the daytime nap, if your child still has one, or phasing it out altogether, to see if that makes any difference. On the other hand, toddlers who still need a daytime nap and who don't get it for one reason or another may need to be put to bed earlier in the evening – and might then end up waking at dawn as a result. It's up to you to judge what will work with your own child. If you take a break in the day, while your child is asleep, this may be more than adequate compensation for an earlier-than-ideal morning.

Early morning strategy for older children

If your child's early rising continues, and none of the above strategies seems to make any difference, you will have to accept the situation. The compensation is that, as your child grows older, the easier it becomes to convince her that early disturbing, as opposed to early waking, is not acceptable.

Older children can cope, luckily, with a few rules about not waking the rest of the household, so that as least they will play quietly in their own rooms and your own sleep will not be too curtailed. An older child (three or four years old) can also be taught to recognize a signal, such as an alarm clock going off in her room (provided she can learn how to switch it off), and told that she is not to wake you before this time. Habitual early-morning waking in an older child can be tempered by the use of star charts and rewards (see pages 48 and 49) for not disturbing the parents too early.

Your child might like to listen to story tapes in the early mornings if she can operate the cassette recorder safely – teach her to keep the volume low. At weekends, provided you are sure the other rooms of your house or flat are safe, you could allow her to watch television quietly – there are cartoons and other children's programmes on from very early in the morning, both at weekends and in the school holidays. Or, if you have a video recorder, you could even put a suitable children's film into the video the night before, for her to switch on and play quietly the next day.

If you get into the habit of putting out your child's clothes the night before, she can get herself washed and dressed, saving time later on.

Parental suggestions

Below are some of the tactics adopted by other parents to put off the moment when they have to get up and start the day. Their relevance will depend on the age of your baby or child, how mobile she is, whether she is in a cot or a bed, and how childproof her, or your, room is. By the time you have tried all of them, no doubt with varying degrees of success, hopefully your child will be at the point of giving up her early start!

"I've found the problem isn't anything like the nuisance it was, since I've put my son into a bed instead of a cot. I don't know what difference it made, really. Perhaps he felt confined in a cot, and feels more comfortable now. He likes being able to get out of bed on his own instead of waiting to be picked up!"

"We brought her into our room, put her on the floor beside the bed, and gave her a bucket of Duplo to play with. She was sitting up, but not yet crawling at this stage. The Duplo was just within my reach if I leaned over a bit and hung an arm out of the bed; I'd hand her different pieces, and 'play' with it one-handed while I dozed – or tried to doze."

"We took it in turns to play with him in 10-minute stretches. He lay between us in our bed and we'd play 'This little piggy' and games like that for as long as he'd last out."

"Once I made sure that the curtains were drawn properly, so the merest chink of dawn light couldn't escape, he started waking a little later."

"Each night before we went to bed we would put a selection of safe toys in his cot, rotating them so he wouldn't get bored with the same ones day after day. That seemed to keep him quiet for a little while each morning before he started shouting for us."

"We left a spouted cup of juice within reach, so he could help himself first thing in the morning. This worked – well, it gave us another five minutes or so – until he learnt to enjoy shaking the liquid out of it like pepper!"

"I made sure her room was as safe as it could be, and put a safety gate across the doorway. She started to quite enjoy getting out of bed herself and playing quietly on her own for up to half an hour."

"The problem wasn't anything like as bad when we put our baby and toddler in the same room. Though the baby was only six months, and her brother was two, he used to wake her up gently, and they'd play together, with him pushing toys for her between the bars of the cot. We'd hear them chatting happily away to each other."

Sleep and the older child

The good news for most parents of wakeful children is that sleeping problems tend to sort themselves out, or get sorted out, in time. By the age of three, the babies who screamed for hours every evening, the toddlers who were waking up and demanding attention several times a night, the children who would protest loudly and passionately about bedtime and the skylarks who prised open your eyelids at five-thirty every morning have, in the main, become lively, energetic children who settle down for bed without a qualm, who lie awake for no more than ten minutes before they drop off into a deep sleep until morning. If you yourself are a light sleeper (or if parenthood has made you become one) you may be aware of a trip to the loo in the middle of the night, or perhaps you hear the taps turned on for a drink of water . . . but otherwise all is silence until a 'sensible' time in the morning. It's then you might hear the rattle of Lego bricks or some childish singing, as your child keeps himself happy until you are ready to begin the day.

If this sounds like bliss and your child is far from being this settled, it may simply be that the change will happen slightly later in his case. You may have worked your life around a wakeful child's habits, but then suddenly the regularity of nursery school, the extended range of activities a growing child is able to enjoy, and his increasing maturity, may all combine to resolve the situation for you just when you had given up hope.

SLEEP NEEDS IN OLDER CHILDREN

Most three- and four-year-olds need something like 12 hours sleep. This may be more than they've ever had before, in some cases. But some children simply don't need as much sleep as others. They function perfectly well on far fewer hours than their friends of similar ages; they may manage well on less sleep than you, in fact.

Plenty of normal children of the same age sleep for only eight, nine or ten hours. This doesn't necessarily mean they're in bed for only that time, however. Nor does it mean that they're actively energetic for all the remaining hours of the day or night, either. If you've had a bedtime routine before now and your wakeful child has come to accept it, the chances are that he's learnt to keep himself happy on his own until he falls asleep.

&6 When my daughter was a year old she needed attention about six times each night. When she went from a cot to a bed it became worse, as she was able to get out and wander into our room. Things have improved over time, however, and now at three she wakes no more than once or twice. 99

Even if your child needs less sleep than others of his age, you may prefer to have him in bed by a certain hour for your own sakes.

If, on the other hand, you have never succeeded in establishing a regular bedtime, it's not too late to introduce one. The added bonus with a child of three or four is that you can explain in words what you want him to do, and he can understand and remember much more readily. Your child's greater understanding also means you can devise simple ways of gaining his co-operation without getting cross or exasperated.

Even if your child is one of those who needs less sleep than others, it's still perfectly reasonable in our society to want to have him in bed by a certain time. Some parents feel guilty about this and are reluctant to insist on an early bedtime because they realize their child doesn't gain anything in particular from going to bed before he's tired. But even non-tired children can benefit from a period of quiet calm, to help them wind down after a busy day. Tell yourself that your child won't come to any harm by being on his own in bed – and that all parents deserve a break. You could allow reading or other quiet activities in bed; this works best if you have a definite rule about how long he has before 'lights out'.

Tiring your child out

A lively three- or four-year-old has bags of energy, and this needs an outlet if your child is to be really tired by the evening. So make your child's days as interesting and varied as you can. Playgroup, toddler group, and regular outings will use up some of his surplus energy. Whenever it's possible, make sure he has a chance to be out of doors for part of the day, on a walk or an outing to the local playground, so that he can run around being active, and get plenty of fresh air.

Just as you would with a younger child, devise a relaxing bedtime routine you can both enjoy. This will help to calm down a lively older child, and put him in the right frame of mind for bed.

Bedtime routine for a wakeful three-year-old

▶ After tea or supper, either play a quiet board or card game, or listen to a story tape with him.

▶ Make bathtime an enjoyable session, when he can splash about and play with water toys. You can chat together about what he's done during the day while you bath him.

▶ You might want to make time for a story, songs, or a chat downstairs, once he is in his pyjamas.

▶ Then up to bed – and a bedtime story or a last few minutes' conversation with you before you tuck him in and say goodnight.

▶ Follow the same bedtime pattern night after night, and don't be persuaded to vary it. Make it clear to your child that it's acceptable for him to look at books, to listen to a story or music tape, or to play with a few soft toys in bed before he goes to sleep. But playing with things out of bed, or coming downstairs, is not allowed.

▶ If your child continually asks for a drink, then leave a beaker of water by his bed so that he can help himself. If he insists that he only wants juice or milk, he can't be truly thirsty, so refuse; this would harm his teeth.

The right environment

Try to make your child's bedroom an attractive place to be, so that he has enough to sustain his interest when left on his own. Let him choose some posters or pictures for his wall, and help him decide how he wants the furniture arranged. Perhaps he can have new curtains, or bedding, with a favourite character on them. All these considerations will help your child to feel that his room is his own special place, and will make him less likely to seek out your company in the evening instead. Some children will lie for an hour or more in bed, awake and attentive, before they feel ready for sleep, and this is fine.

THE OVER-TIRED CHILD

It's quite possible for a child to need more sleep as he grows, not less. For example, children who start full-time school at four or five often seem to become more tired because of the social and educational demands made on them. Watch out for signs of increased tiredness, which may include cross and irritable behaviour in the mornings and in the evenings. Some children end up 'flopping around', bored and aimless but not apparently sleepy, in the afternoons and evenings. Bringing bedtime forward is the best strategy for dealing with this.

It will help some children to be less grumpy in the early evening if they have been given a chance to unwind when they get home from school. Let your child watch children's television or just relax on the sofa with you if that calms him and allows him to rest – he may even drop off to sleep. It's not a good idea to let the snooze last a long time if your child is generally reluctant to go to bed in the evening, or has a tendency to wake through the night, however.

Q My three-year-old son used to be a good sleeper. He needed the usual night feeds as a baby, but at five months he began sleeping through the night. By the time he was eight months old, I had a very good routine going: he'd be asleep by seven in the evening and I wouldn't hear him until seven the next morning. He had a two-hour daytime nap as well.

Everything's changed now, however. In the last two months he's started waking up and crying, and recently this has become more frequent. At first I thought he was upset about something, and I was concerned to give him the reassurance he needed. But now I'm convinced he's just waking up because he's got used to the idea. Is there anything I can do?

A This isn't uncommon. Children's sleep patterns change without any apparent reason. It may be that your son had a bad dream, or a pain, or was woken up by a noise on one or two occasions. You did exactly the right thing and comforted him. It does seem, however, that he's forgotten how to get himself back to sleep without help. Leave a favourite toy in bed with him, and be extra reassuring at bedtime. Check that there's nothing frightening, unpleasant or uncomfortable about his bed or his room (see page 31). Tell him that you want to go back to sleeping through yourself – at three he'll understand. When he wakes, give him the minimum attention needed to settle him – he might even be reassured by hearing your voice from another room. Or use the star chart idea to give him an incentive. He's very likely to go back to his previous settled routine before long, without distress.

BRIBERY AND CORRUPTION?

Old habits die hard, and if you are trying to establish a bedtime routine for an older child, it may take some time and a lot of perseverence. Rather than ending up getting cross with your child, you could make the new sleeping regime a challenge and a positive achievement in itself. A three-year-old will readily understand a star chart, which rewards good behaviour without punishing bad behaviour.

Draw up a weekly chart based on the one shown on the following page, with a space beside each day. Depending on the age of your child, he could help to write in the days of the week, or at least decorate the chart. On each day that he does what you want him to do with regard to bedtime arrangements and sleeping, you award a star. You can either buy stick-on stars, or draw them in by hand. It may seem surprising, but children get a buzz from the star itself, and you may not have to promise any material reward at the end of a successful week. It may help, though, to decide that five stars on the trot, or five out of seven, means some sort of treat, agreed on in advance.

Family evenings

If you really don't mind having your child's company all evening, and your child is healthy and lively on less sleep than his friends, then you don't have a problem. Once at school, your child will also come across children who stay up later than him, and who therefore watch more late-night television, and he may feel he should be allowed more leniency. Remember, though, that with your child's growing understanding, he may be more affected by, and involved in, television programmes that the rest of the family might watch later in the evening.

Currently in the UK the 'watershed' hour for family viewing is nine o'clock – that is, programmes shown after that time may have a content that is considered unsuitable for young children. But some of the more gritty soaps or documentaries on earlier than this may well cover topics you don't want your young child to be exposed to. If you do have your child up with you in the evenings, you might bear this in mind and consider which television programmes you should simply stop watching.

You'll know best what will appeal to your child, but make it small. Don't allow yourself to be manipulated into awarding bigger and better treats. Ten pence, a box of Smarties, or a comic are all quite lavish enough for a weekly reward.

A variation on the star chart might be a sticker chart, as shown below, or a sticker album. You provide the album, and the stickers, bought separately, are awarded one by one as a reward for cooperative behaviour.

With a sticker chart (below), your child 'earns' a sticker for every night he sleeps through.

A star chart (right) uses stars to mark the good nights; five or more a week might earn a reward.

— KATIE'S STICKER CHART —

	Mon	Tues	Wed	Thurs	Fri	Sat	Sun
Week 1			⚙		🧸		
Week 2	🦢	⛵		🎺			
Week 3		🥁		🎺	⚙		🎺
Week 4	🎺		🧸	⛵	🦢		
Week 5	⛵	🧸	🧸	🦢		⛵	🍦

BEDWETTING

At the age of three, half of all children are still wet at night. Most of these are dry by five and a further proportion by the age of seven; only about one in 20 children is still wet at this age. The ability to stay dry at night is linked with wakefulness in certain children. As they grow older, some children become more aware of being wet at night and they wake up as a result; this is not invariable, however – other children remain fast asleep throughout.

To minimize the disturbance of your sleep, you can teach a bedwetting child over about six to service himself in the night. Show him how to get clean pyjamas, remove the wet plastic sheet and bedsheet and replace them with clean ones; obviously you won't expect 'hospital corners' on the newly-tucked-in sheet, as long as it gets on the bed somehow. The wet pyjamas and sheets should be placed in a plastic bag for you to deal with in the morning. Leave all the clean gear together in an easy-to-reach place.

Most bedwetting clinics – outpatient clinics at hospitals and health centres – and doctors won't consider giving any form of therapy to children who wet the bed under the age of seven because so many grow out of the tendency by themselves by this age. There are many theories about the causes of continued bedwetting, but no proof that there are necessarily any underlying medical or psychiatric reasons. But when an older child continues to wet the bed, it causes understandable concern to the families involved, and embarrassment and a dread of bedtime to the child himself.

You can try to help your child become dry before the age of seven. Some children are just late developers in this respect, however, and the suggestions overleaf may not work for them.

~ ALEX'S STAR CHART ~	
Monday 20th	⭐
Tuesday 21st	Up in the night
Wednesday 22nd	⭐
Thursday 23rd	Tried to come in with Mum and Dad
Friday 24th	⭐
Saturday 25th	⭐
Sunday 26th	⭐
Notes	Getting better!

Helping your child to stay dry at night

▶ If your child is in nappies at three, just try leaving them off for a few nights and seeing what happens (use a plastic sheet over the mattress). Removing the nappy may remove the 'permission' to pee in it, and will help the child's unconscious control.

▶ Insist on a last-minute visit to the lavatory just before your child goes to bed.

▶ As a last resort, 'lift' your child as you go to bed and help him to use the lavatory. Wake him up to do this, as you want him to recognize the sensation of a full bladder and to respond to it while conscious. Pee-ing while still asleep or half-asleep, is exactly what you want him to *stop* doing.

▶ Star charts can help a great deal with night-time dryness – but you should abandon the chart if it doesn't bring about an improvement in a week or so. You can always try again a few weeks later.

▶ Don't cut down on drinks at bedtime: your child will go to bed thinking about drinks and may wake with a genuine thirst. There is no evidence that a drink at bedtime causes bedwetting.

▶ Be positive – praising dry nights and ignoring wet ones is more effective than punishing wet nights.

Once your child is in a bed, he has greater independence and may endlessly reappear, ever confident of a welcome.

Sleep problems

Many sleep difficulties – such as wakefulness and crying, bedtime tantrums, night-time waking, early-morning energy, lack of a routine – are eventually accepted by most parents as normal, if they go on for long enough. You might be exhausted, you might feel inadequate and guilty from time to time, but you know they will not go on forever, and the conversations you have with other parents convince you that plenty of other children react in the same way. But there are some sleep-related problems that are less common, and, to the families involved, these are usually much more worrying.

CONSTANT CRYING

There are some babies who cry constantly, who won't be pacified by the breast, bottle or dummy, even when offered continually, and who are never happy for more than a few minutes at a time. These babies hardly ever fall asleep contented but simply drop off with exhaustion, and when awake seem genuinely distressed and sometimes even in pain. Even when they aren't actually crying, they are tense and look as if they're about to begin again at any second. They need constant cuddling, rocking and soothing. Of course, many babies are like this some of the time, but if yours is like this on most days, it is a situation which can become desperate. If you're the mother or father of such a baby, you need help and support (see Useful Addresses, page 63).

The 'average' baby cries for a total of around two hours a day, but these crying babies have been known to spend up to nine hours a day screaming inconsolably. The cause may be one of several and you may never find out what has brought about the crying in your baby's particular case. Excessive crying does usually stop after the first three months, though a few babies carry on crying for most of their first year. Below are some possible reasons for this desperate crying which would be worth investigating. (The more obvious ones of hunger, loneliness, boredom, heat and cold are covered elsewhere.)

Possible causes of crying

▶ A 'headache'. It does appear that a few babies develop a lasting headache as a result of the way the bones of the skull become moved in childbirth. Manipulation by an osteopath who can perform cranial osteopathy has been known to give tremendous relief to these babies, and to stop the crying. Ask your doctor to refer you to a reputable osteopath if you think this might help.

▶ Food sensitivity. A few babies are sensitive to cows' milk (the milk on which baby formula is based); these babies often show other symptoms too, such as poor weight gain. Cows' milk intolerance

Possible causes of crying (continued)

needs a proper diagnosis – don't switch your baby's formula without it – but, once diagnosed, you can use a special baby formula available on prescription. It is also possible to build up your milk supply so you can return to breastfeeding your baby, though this requires great commitment and motivation. A breastfeeding counsellor (see Useful Addresses, page 63) will be able to help.

▶ Food intolerance in a breast-fed baby. Some babies respond adversely to minute traces of certain foods in the mother's breast milk. You can alter your diet by a process of elimination to identify an offending item. The most common culprits seem to be milk, eggs, coffee and cola drinks. Make sure you don't go without important nutrients if you change your diet permanently.

Repeated crying in the first three months is often attributed to 'colic', though some doctors do not recognize this as a medical condition. The main features are that the child screams inconsolably, apparently in pain, and usually at a regular time, often the evening. If your child's crying and discomfort do seem to be related to digestion, there is a drug which your doctor will prescribe, that helps to relax the muscles lining the gut.

The idea of bedsharing suits many families for a time; the older the child gets, however, the less comfortable it becomes!

Babies who are ill cry a lot; very occasionally, parents of babies who are handicapped report a miserable, desolate first few months of constant crying. However, when there is anything seriously wrong, there are almost always other symptoms. If you feel that the crying is an indication of a real problem with your baby, then seek medical advice. Keep a 'crying diary' if you feel this will help a doctor to take you more seriously. Lots of babies cry 'a lot' – and a diary shows just how much.

HEAD-BANGING

This refer to the baby who repeatedly bangs her head against a hard surface – usually the end of her cot – deliberately and rhythmically. One study showed that seven per cent of under-ones head-bang at some stage, so it couldn't be called uncommon. The habit usually starts in late infancy and most babies and toddlers stop in a matter of months. But it may carry on throughout toddlerhood, ending not later than around the age of three (and often long before). The sessions last anything from a few minutes to (rarely) a few hours and take place either before sleep, or during sleep, or when a child wakes in the night. Sometimes, the head-banging child makes a red, raised mark on her head or forehead as a result of severe banging. It would make sense to pad the ends of your child's cot to reduce the chance of a sore head.

Medical experts are divided on whether head-banging in infants is a serious cause for concern. In most children it's a habit, pure and simple, that the child has discovered for herself, but in some cases it *may* be a sign of unhappiness, lack of security, anger or stress. It's always worth discussing the situation with your health visitor or your doctor – especially if, over time, the head-banging habit becomes more insistent, or increases in intensity and frequency.

❝ Tom is now aged 19 months, and shows no signs of stopping the head-banging he began when he was just a few months old. He does it mostly when he's trying to get to sleep, and sometimes when he's tired in the day he'll crawl on to my knee and try to do the same thing against my shoulder. ❞

THE HYPERACTIVE CHILD

Never make the mistake of assuming that your wakeful child is hyperactive. Hyperactivity is not just wakefulness, or resistance to going to bed, though most hyperactive children seem to need very little sleep indeed, and their wakefulness, and energy throughout the night, may be among the worst effects of the condition. Hyperactive children also have a range of behaviour problems including excessive, aggressive energy, difficulties in communicating, speech delay, extreme food fads and crazes, and violent mood swings. Some cynics dismiss the whole notion of hyperactivity by describing such children as 'hyper-naughty', but this condition is in fact a real and distressing one, and totally exhausting for the parents involved.

With some hyperactive children there is a definite link with food sensitivity, so strong in some cases that the child becomes transformed when the offending item or items are taken out of the diet. Additives such as colouring may be to blame; with other children it may be milk, eggs, wheat or certain fruits (such as oranges). The only way to find out is to omit each possible offender for several days (difficult with some children who may be 'addicted' to the very food that harms them) and then re-introduce it as a challenge. To get help in doing this, contact a support group (see Useful Addresses, page 63) and get your doctor involved, too. Don't manipulate your child's diet permanently without making sure it still has the necessary nutrients in it.

Changing the diet is only one possible way of helping a hyperactive child. Your doctor will advise you about others, including drugs and behaviour therapy, and contacting a support group will make you feel that you are less alone.

" Ben was just impossible; I couldn't get through to him at all on some days, and he never slept for more than an hour at a time. Eventually, I cut out all artificial colourings and the difference was amazing. He became a changed child. "

NIGHTMARES

Having a 'bad dream' is a horrible experience even for an adult – but at least when you wake up you know it's a dream. How much more distressing it must be for a baby or child, who is hardly aware of the difference between imagination and reality. Nightmares in children occur most commonly between the ages of eight and ten.

Studies show that babies have the Rapid Eye Movement (REM) sleep associated with dreams in older children and adults. If your baby wakes up and starts to scream for no apparent reason, and needs a lot of comforting to settle down again, one strong possibility is that she has had a bad dream. After a nightmare, a child of any age will wake up quite terrified for a few minutes, and an older child will be able to tell you something of what she's dreamt about. The important thing is to get to your child as quickly as possible, and to hold and cuddle her. You should be able to calm and reassure her within a few minutes. Try to take her mind off the nightmare by talking about something pleasant instead. Leave any questioning about the content of the nightmare until the morning.

The occasional nightmare is part of childhood – part of life, even. Repeated nightmares, whether or not they're about the same subject, are often a symptom of unhappiness, or an underlying fear or anxiety. A major upset that happened years before – like a divorce or death – can sometimes cause nightmares, as if the unconscious mind refuses to stay silent in its distress. Sensitive counselling and, if necessary, help from a child or family guidance centre, can often reveal hidden anxieties that are causing the nightmares.

NIGHT-TIME FEARS

Fears of the dark, or of bedtime, can develop in a child who has previously been happy enough about both (see page 31). You can sometimes pinpoint the cause quite easily – such as a recent burglary, or a worry about being on her own because she's had a frightening experience. Or perhaps your child has seen a vivid television programme, or read a book that has sparked off her imagination. These fears can be very real to a child at night-time, even though during the day she can probably convince herself that she has nothing to worry about.

If your child has a vivid imagination, then it will help if you 'censor' television programmes or books that are known to be frightening. Certainly don't let her watch or read them just before going to bed, or thinking about them afterwards will make her too anxious to get to sleep. In some cases, you may be unaware what has triggered off a particular night-time fear. But if a group of children have been talking about something frightening – such as ghosts – this may have preyed on her mind.

Night-time fears can often be 'cured' by helping your child to gain control over them. If she's frightened about monsters, for example, read some funny stories that will 'demystify' them. But always be sympathetic, understanding and reassuring about any night fears your child may have. Let her have a light on in her room at night (see the illustration of different night lights on page 32) and see if that helps.

❝ My daughter's seven, and a few months ago she saw a television programme about ghosts that frightened her. She's now very scared of anything, such as a shadow or a noise, that could be interpreted as a ghost. She can make herself stay awake until midnight, terrified to fall asleep. ❞

NIGHT TERRORS

A night terror is different from a nightmare. Night terrors occur in toddlers and older children when the child is asleep, though she may actually have her eyes wide open during the experience, looking staring and terrified. It's quite obvious to an observer that the child is going through a frightening experience – she may scream and shout, wave her arms and toss and turn; she may even run round the room. Such episodes last up to half an hour, and in a badly affected child, they may happen every night, or most nights, for years – sometimes even more than once a night. Afterwards the child calms down and later on cannot remember anything of what happened.

It's obviously very distressing for the family when a child has a night terror. The parents' attention is usually drawn by the shouts and general agitation coming from the child's room, only to find when they get there that she is going through this experience in her sleep. Fortunately, there seem to be no long-term ill effects, and all affected children grow out of night terrors eventually.

" For the last year my three-year-old son has been waking up in the evenings. He starts to scream "Mummy", yet when I go in to cuddle and reassure him he starts to struggle with me, screaming "no!". There's nothing I can do to calm him, since he doesn't really respond to me. After half an hour he flops back onto his pillow, sobbing a little, and then settles down. This happens about three times every week. "

It used to be assumed that night terrors must be a sign of underlying anxiety. More recently, however, the whole phenomenon is thought to be a result of disturbed sleep rhythms. Much beneficial work has been done in sleep clinics to stop night terrors. The solution involves waking the child up about 15 minutes before the night terror is expected (since they often occur at around the same time each night) or – if their timing is less predictable – just as the child starts to twitch or moan. If you do this for several days on the run, it usually effects a cure – probably because you are giving the child's body a chance to establish new rhythms.

SLEEPWALKING

Sleepwalking occurs in the very deepest phase of sleep and the walker remembers nothing of it the next day. It is an eerie thing to watch, as the 'subject' is definitely asleep, though her eyes may be open. After moving around her room, or other areas of the house, the sleepwalker usually ends by taking herself back to bed. Studies show that sleepwalking is more common in boys than in girls, and that it's most likely to happen between the ages of five and 10. It's not thought to be a sign of emotional disturbance in any way and most children grow out of it.

Since sleep walkers *can* injure themselves, you need to make sure the walker's environment is safe: put a safety gate at the top of the stairs, for example, and make sure windows are kept shut at night. Take the child back to bed as soon as you see what's happening – there will be no objections.

" Nicola started sleepwalking when she was just three. She manages to walk downstairs without falling, and to push open doors — it's very strange. She usually sleepwalks at the same time, about 11 o'clock. We've always simply turned her round and taken her back to bed. Over the last two years the episodes have become less frequent. She's now eight and a half, and I expect she'll stop soon. "

You and your sleepless child

Sleep deprivation is a well-known form of torture, and long-term loss of sleep can cause both emotional and psychiatric disorders. In the short term, as most parents experience at some time, a 'bad night' or two can leave you feeling not only tired but generally out of sorts the next day.

Before you had a baby, things were different. After a late night, or one during which for some reason you've tossed and turned and been unable to get much sleep, you were probably able to have a lie-in the next day – at worst, you could wait until the weekend and catch up then. With a baby at home, you may have a late night – and a broken one – but there's no possibility of having a lie-in the next day. The situation is the same at weekends. Not only must you get up early, you also have to face a demanding, sometimes exhausting, day with only unpredictable prospects of a break. However you feel, you carry the ongoing responsibility for the day-to-day care of your child, so you have to be as alert as possible.

The broken-nights aspect of parenthood is one of the key reasons for any stress and unhappiness experienced by families with a young baby. After all the waiting, the high that comes from having delivered a baby, the terrific sense of achievement you get from the interest and praise given by family and friends . . . after only a few weeks, all this can seem insignificant compared with the longer-lasting reality of day-to-day, and night-to-night, fatigue.

Endless disturbed nights can catch up on you at the most inappropriate time!

FAMILY STRESS

Having a new baby in the house is a recognized major life change, and it's not necessarily one that always brings you closer together as a couple. You may have to work hard at seeing the positive side of parenthood, by talking about the love you both have for this little person, however disruptive he is, taking pleasure together in seeing him grow and develop, getting to know other parents and sharing experiences, good and bad, with them.

Most couples who have a sleepless child end up arguing about the situation at some time, however – even if it's only in the middle of the night, when you dispute whose turn it is to deal with the problem! It is important that you both recognize the stress you are under, discuss the problem fully, and share the burden of your wakeful child. Try to be optimistic that this stage is only temporary and will not last forever. Talk to friends who have older children and you will realize that this trying behaviour will come to an end.

Don't feel guilty if you are disappointed with the reality of new parenthood. Don't blame yourself for having a wakeful baby and, above all, don't think it's because you don't know enough about being a parent that your baby won't sleep. A newborn baby does not 'sense' that his mother is lacking in confidence, and refuse to sleep because he picks up her stress. It's true that families with a wakeful baby are more likely to be stressed, but this is a *result* of the wakefulness, not a cause of it.

Hardly anyone feels totally capable, at first, of looking after a new baby all by themselves, but they muddle through, somehow, and gradually gain in confidence as time goes on. Your baby wants love, security, warmth and food – and he makes sure that he gets it. He couldn't care less if you feel serene – and he won't even notice if you're still in your dressing gown at lunchtime! It will help you to cope better with your baby if you accept that, for the moment, his basic needs are all that matter, and that other things belong way down the list. If you worked before having a baby, you might have imagined that being home-based would mean you had time for lots of extra household chores. Forget these for the time being.

Catching up on sleep

With your first baby, you can go some way towards catching up on rest and sleep – but not on the ironing – by following some of the tips below from other parents.

None of these suggestions is easy to follow if you have other children, unfortunately. You may need to read a story, or build a Lego man, or roll out playdough, while feeding the baby. It's a matter of grabbing what rest you can when you get the opportunity – and accepting any offers of help you may have.

- ▶ Sleep whenever your baby sleeps during the day.
- ▶ Lie down to breastfeed your baby.
- ▶ If you do something else while feeding, such as reading, watching television or listening to the radio, it helps you to unwind and relax properly.
- ▶ Go to bed earlier in the evening.

TIME TO YOURSELF

You should never allow yourself to become so wrapped up in your baby that your own needs become non-existent. Even when your baby is very young, try to get a little time on your own. It won't be very long if your baby's breast-fed, but even an hour or so out of the house, for a walk, or a trip to the library, or coffee at a friend's house, can feel wonderful. Accept some of those offers to 'babysit any time' that you had from friends and relatives when the baby was born. People are very glad to help, on the whole, once you acknowledge a need.

The company of a demanding, sleepless baby needs to be tempered by the company of adults who actually talk to you. Join a toddler group (most accept babies as well), or find your nearest branch of the National Childbirth Trust. Many NCT branches run neighbourhood groups especially for parents and young babies, and will offer one-to-one postnatal support if you need it – see Useful Addresses, page 63. Your health visitor will help you get in touch with other new mothers if you don't know many others in your area: don't be too shy to nurture new friends. Meeting and talking to other parents will give you the moral support of those who are going through, or have gone through, the same experiences – and survived!

❝ Looking back, I'm quite sure I would have hated every minute of my baby's first few months if I hadn't found other mothers. She didn't sleep much during the day, and I couldn't keep her entertained. My health visitor told me about the toddler group — I felt desperate enough to be brave and I just turned up there. Everyone was really friendly. I got to know a lot of people, and from then on I began to feel a part of the community in a way I had never been before. ❞

SEEKING HELP

Never be afraid to ask for help if you are finding it hard to cope with your sleepless, wakeful baby. Speak to your doctor, health visitor or midwife – or contact a support group (see Useful Addresses), and don't leave it until things are absolutely desperate before doing so. Too many parents, thinking that excessive crying must be normal (see page 51) or that it's in some way their fault, struggle on, presenting a falsely brave face to the world.

You can get sympathy and information from many of the addresses listed on page 63. In addition, some areas have special 'sleep clinics' that aim to help families solve sleeping problems through counselling and support. They may be run as an outpatient clinic in a hospital, or at a local health centre. Your doctor or your health visitor should know, or be able to find out, about any sleep clinics in your area, and it would be worth visiting one if you are feeling desperate. It will at least make you realize that you are not alone.

It is important for your relationship that you have some time together, away from the baby – provided you can stay awake to enjoy it!

❝ Melanie is six, and has recently started to come into our bed – something she hasn't wanted to do since she was a toddler. She comes into our room, saying she can't sleep, then climbs in with us and is there until morning. My husband feels we should show love to her, and not rejection, but I worry in case we're starting a habit that will be hard to break. ❞

By the time your baby is older, and still not sleeping much, the sympathy and understanding shown to you by other people may be wearing thin. 'Surely he's not still waking up?' you might be asked regularly, by people who imply that you ought to be doing 'something' about it now. If you're feeling tired, then a sense of inadequacy mixed with a certain defensive attitude makes you feel even lower. You may well be trying to change your baby's wakeful habits, without success. But even if you're not, remember that doing something about it is not in any way compulsory.

You might feel that you are getting better at coping with broken nights, you might at times quite enjoy those moments in the dark with your child, sharing a feeling of closeness and love. You may have developed a bearable routine by now, and feel resigned to accepting the way things are for the present and be optimistic about the future. The chances are that you have discovered something that sends your baby back to sleep – whether it's a breastfeed, a dummy, a cuddle in your bed – without intolerable disruption. Whatever it is, feel confident that your way of dealing with things is perfectly acceptable.

YOUR PARTNER'S SUPPORT

The person you should turn to most readily when your baby's wakefulness is getting you down is, of course, your partner. Truly burdensome nights need to be shared out, in all fairness. A child who regularly wakes and needs a lot of attention to get back to sleep again shouldn't affect one parent disproportionately. For the child who insists that only mum (or dad) will do at night, you need to be very consistent about taking turns in order to get your child to accept that both of you are equally capable of settling him at night. Teaching him to accept comfort from someone else will at least give you a break and allow you to get some unbroken sleep.

Make sure you and your partner feel the same way about handling your child's problem when it comes to a change of policy. If one of you is prepared to accept your child's sleeping habits, and the other partner wants to change them, this will only be an extra source of stress. The parent who deals most with the broken nights will end up forfeiting sympathy from the other; the one who wants to change will become more and more irritated, and less willing to put up with inconveniences such as bedsharing.

Don't let your child exploit a difference of opinion – or just the difference in willpower. It's extraordinary how clever even a very young child is at realizing what he can try with which parent. Once you have decided that a night-time wanderer will be put straight back into bed without a story/drink/sing-song/cuddle in your bed, for example, then you must both stick at this and back each other up. Otherwise your plan of action will simply not even begin to work.

Use a quiet time, when you're on your own without your child, to discuss new ideas for managing your child's sleep problems. Don't do it when you feel cross with your partner, or vice versa, or are in a mood of resentment. Accept that tiredness can lead to stress, and that it's all to easy to take out your feelings on the person closest to you.

Make sure you and your partner have times alone, when you can enjoy each other's company without worrying about being disturbed by your baby or child. This can mean a regular night out, or even a regular afternoon in, when someone else looks after your baby. You needn't go out on the town, especially if you are tired, but even a drink at the local pub makes a change.

If both of you work, you'll need to make even more of an effort to find time to be together, as well as time to rest and to catch up on lost sleep. Think about changing your working hours to suit you better, if that's possible. More and more employers are willing to allow a weekly day working at home, or to accept more flexible hours to avoid the rush. If you can reduce stress in other areas of your life, you'll be better able to cope with your child's wakefulness.

Sexual deprivation?

You might hear people joking that the best contraceptive of all is having a baby – broken nights and extreme fatigue don't go with a spontaneous and active sex life. You will almost certainly find you don't make love as often as you used to – and that, even when the chance arises, the idea of sleep itself is sometimes infinitely more attractive!

" Our babies always slept in the same room as us in the first few months of life, to make night feeds easier. But I could never relax enough to make love if there was a baby in the cradle beside me. So, before settling down to love-making we'd move baby and cradle into another room. **"**

Lots of parents manage the adjustment perfectly well, though, and learn to accept that it is quite usual to start love-making, only to be put off your stride by the sound of a whimper from the next room. That whimper might die down – or it might build up to an attention-needing cry. And what do you know? You've somehow lost the urge . . . You might find you have to stage-manage your sex life, and make love when the opportunity's there, such as when your wakeful toddler has been taken out for a Saturday afternoon walk by granny. The reality is that people's sex lives, and their sexual desire, ebb and flo. Sex is a part of life and subject to major influences (such as having babies) that may curtail it, but which can also enhance and change it. So don't worry if your sex life virtually disappears for a time after having a baby. Unless it's actually painful to have intercourse (in which case seek medical help) just wait until you both feel ready and show your love for each other in different ways in the meantime.

Don't ever let sleepless nights drive you apart. Supporting each other through the difficult times, and sharing the problem by talking about it and doing whatever you can to bear with it, or to solve it, can bring you and your partner closer together emotionally than ever before.

Coping alone

A wakeful child is especially hard to cope with if you're on your own, either because you're a single parent or because your partner is often away. It's all too easy to blame yourself, and to become stressed because you can't share the burden with someone else who cares.

Never think 'it's all my fault'. Sleepless children exist in families in all sorts of circumstances. Try to seek out sympathetic help during the day, to give yourself the chance to catch up on your own sleep. Perhaps a grandparent, sister, or a good friend would take your child overnight occasionally.

Parenting alone can be very difficult, even when you aren't tired. Remember that you need to look after yourself, as well as your child – if only for your child's sake. Groups for single parents can give you some emotional and practical help. If your partner is sometimes there – perhaps he works away for nights or weeks on end – it can be tempting not to admit to difficulties because you want to welcome him back to a family without problems or stress. But don't pretend: share your feelings and let him know what life is really like when he's not there with you.

Useful addresses

The following groups and associations offer different kinds of information and support to help you deal with a wakeful child. Always send a stamped addressed envelope when writing for information.

National Childbirth Trust
Alexandra House
Oldham Terrace
London W3 6NH
(081) 992 8637
Antenatal education, breastfeeding counselling and postnatal support. See your local telephone directory for local branches.

Association for Postnatal Illness
7 Gowan Avenue
London SW6
(071) 731 4867
Local counsellors – mothers who have recovered from postnatal depression – give support and information to mothers going through this illness.

Association of Breastfeeding Mothers
Sydenham Green Health Centre
26 Holmshaw Close
London SE26 4TH
(081) 778 4769
Breastfeeding advice, information and support.

CRY-SIS
BM CRY-SIS
London WC1N 3XX
(071) 404 5011
Network of local contacts to give counselling support and information to parents of crying babies.

Hyperactive Children's Support Group
c/o 71 Whyke Lane
Chichester
West Sussex PO9 2LD
Network of groups and local contacts. Diet sheets.

La Leche League
BM 3424
London WC1N 3XX
(071) 242 1278
Breastfeeding advice, information and support.

Useful books

THE COMPLETE MOTHERCARE MANUAL (Conran Octopus)
Everything you need to know from pregnancy to school-age children.

FOOD FOR THOUGHT Maureen Minchin (Oxford University Press)
Sound advice on food intolerance.

MY CHILD WON'T SLEEP Jo Douglas and Naomi Richman (Penguin)
Practical guidelines based on experience in a sleep clinic.

THREE IN A BED Deborah Jackson (Bloomsbury)
A frank and enthusiastic encouragement to parents who are thinking of sharing their bed with their child. Outlines many positive aspects.

THE BABY AND CHILD BOOK Doctors Andrew and Penny Stanway (Pan)
Child-centred approach to childcare; supportive, comprehensive and realistic.

Index